TEACHER'S RESOURCE MASTERS

BLACKLINE MASTERS AND TEACHER'S MANUAL

GRADE **3**

SHARE
the
Music

M A C M I L L A N
M c G R A W - H I L L

SERIES AUTHORS

Judy Bond
Coordinating Author

René Boyer-White

Margaret Campbelle-duGard

Marilyn Copeland Davidson
Coordinating Author

Robert de Frece

Mary Goetze
Coordinating Author

Doug Goodkin

Betsy M. Henderson

Michael Jothen

Carol King

Vincent P. Lawrence
Coordinating Author

Nancy L. T. Miller

Ivy Rawlins

Susan Snyder
Coordinating Author

Contributing Writer
Janet McMillion

Macmillan/McGraw-Hill School Publishing Company
New York • Columbus

INTRODUCTION

This *Teacher's Resource Masters* book contains supplementary activities for *Share the Music.*

The Resource Masters include the following:

- A variety of activities that reinforce or review concepts taught in the lessons. Some Resource Masters emphasize manipulative activities, while others offer written and aural activities.

- Listening maps that provide visual guidance for students as they listen to specific music selections. The listening maps help students identify melodic and rhythmic patterns, tone color, form, and other musical elements.

- Assessment questions for each unit. The assessment questions and music examples are recorded. Two recorded options are available for each question.

- Scripts for musicals.

- Tools for Assessment, including portfolio and self-assessment forms.

- An answer key.

All Resource Masters may be duplicated for classroom use. Each is keyed into the Teacher's Edition. A line at the bottom of the Resource Master identifies the page in the Teacher's Edition with which the Resource Master is intended to be used.

For listening maps, teaching suggestions are provided on the back of the Resource Master.

ACKNOWLEDGMENTS

Grateful acknowledgment is given to the following authors, composers, and publishers. Every effort has been made to trace the ownership of all copyrighted material and to secure the necessary permissions to reprint these selections. In the case of some selections for which acknowledgment is not given, extensive research has failed to locate the copyright holders.

CPP/Belwin, Inc. for *We're Off to See the Wizard* by E. Y. Harburg and Harold Arlen. Copyright © 1938, 1939 (Renewed 1966, 1967) METRO-GOLDWYN MAYER, INC., Rights assigned to EMI CATALOGUE PARTNERSHIP. All rights controlled and administered by EMI FEIST CATALOGUE, INC. International copyright secured. Made in USA. All rights reserved.

Little, Brown and Company for *The Umbrella Brigade* from TIRRA LIRRA: RHYMES OLD AND NEW by Laura E. Richards. Copyright 1930, 1932 by Laura E. Richards. Copyright © renewed 1960 by Hamilton Richards. By permission of Little, Brown and Company.

Sundance Music for *The Electric Cat* by Linda Worsley. Copyright © 1988 Sundance Music.

Contributing Writer
Angela Broeker

Macmillan/McGraw-Hill School Division
10 Union Square East
New York, New York 10003

Printed in the United States of America

ISBN 0-02-295088-5 / 3

2 3 4 5 6 7 8 9 MAL 99 98 97 96 95 94

TABLE OF CONTENTS

Macmillan/McGraw-Hill

		TEACHER'S EDITION page	RESOURCE MASTERS page

Macmillan/McGraw-Hill

Macmillan/McGraw-Hill

Bonefish, Bluebird

Clap the beat as you say "Bonefish, Bluebird." Say
it again clapping the rhythm of the words.

Bonefish, Bluebird

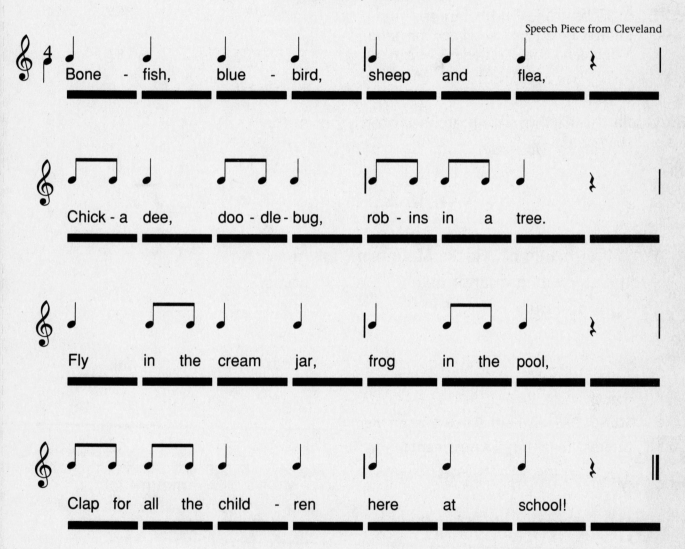

Speech Piece from Cleveland

Name ________________________________

RESOURCE MASTER 1•2 Practice

Rocky Mountain Rhythms

1. Circle the quarter note.

   a. ♩ b. ♫ c. 𝄽

2. Box the beamed eighth notes.

   a. ♩ b. ♫ c. 𝄽

3. Circle the rhythm that matches the rhythm of the words *Rocky Mountain*.

   a. 𝅗𝅥 𝅗𝅥 b. ♫ ♩ c. ♫ ♫

4. Write the rhythm of "Rocky Mountain." Fill in each blank with a quarter note (♩), eighth notes (♫), or a quarter rest (𝄽).

________	________	________	________
Rock - y	moun - tain,	Rock - y	moun - tain,
________	________	________	________
Rock - y	moun - tain,	high.	

(See answers at the back of this book.)

Name_____

More Rocky Mountain Rhythms

1. Clap these rhythms.

a.

b.

c.

2. Write the word to match the rhythm. Add the bar lines.

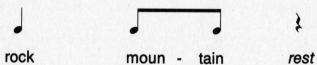

rock   moun - tain   *rest*

a.

_____   _____   _____   _____

b.

_____   _____   _____   _____

c.

_____   _____   _____   _____

d.

_____   _____   _____   _____

3. Now clap the rhythm and say the words.

(See answers at the back of this book.)

RESOURCE MASTER 1•4 Practice

Show Your Skill with a Staff

A staff has five lines and four spaces that are
numbered from the bottom up.

1. Write the number of the space or the line toward
   which the arrow points.

   a. _____    **c.** _____

   b. _____    **d.** _____

2. Draw notes.

   a. 1st line 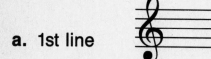   **c.** 3rd space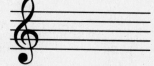

   b. 5th line 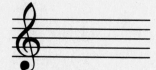   **d.** 1st space

3. Look at these pitch syllables from "Kuma San."

   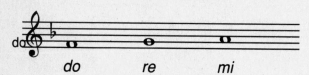

   Write *do re* or *mi* below each note.

   _____ _____ _____ _____

   Count the number of correct answers: _____
   How did you do? 10–12 = Super Staffer
                   7–9 = Almost There
                   4–6 = On Your Way
                   1–3 = Try Again

   (See answers at the back of this book.)

Macmillan/McGraw-Hill

Do is in the first space in the song "Dumplin's."
Write the pitch syllables for these *do re mi* patterns.

1.

2.

Write the letter to match the *do re mi* syllables with
the notation.

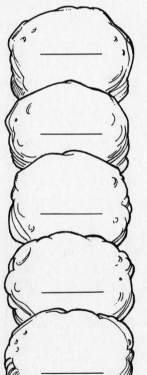

3. *mi   mi   do*   **a.**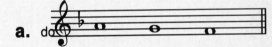

4. *do   re   mi*   **b.**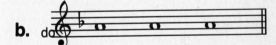

5. *mi   mi   mi*   **c.**

6. *mi   re   do*   **d.**

7. *do   re   do*   **e.**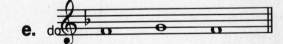

(See answers at the back of this book.)

Macmillan/McGraw-Hill

RESOURCE MASTER 1•6 Practice

Roving Rhythms

Cut out and arrange the following rhythms to create
your own four-beat roving rhythm.

"A-Rovin'" Lyrics

Sing these words as you listen to "A-Rovin'."

1. In Amsterdam there lived a maid, Mark well what I do say.
In Amsterdam there lived a maid Of beauty rare, and so I stayed;
I'll go no more a-rovin' from you, fair maid.

Refrain
A-rovin', a-rovin', a-rovin', it's been my ruin.
I'll go no more a-rovin' with you fair maid.

2. I took this fair maid for a walk, Mark well what I do say.
I took this fair maid for a walk, And we did have a lovely talk;
I'll go no more a-rovin' from you, fair maid.

Refrain

Check It Out

1. You will hear a song with a drum playing along.
 What is the drum playing?
   a. the rhythm   **b.** the beat   **c.** changes from rhythm to beat

2. You will hear a song with a drum playing along.
 What is the drum playing?
   a. the rhythm   **b.** the beat   **c.** changes from rhythm to beat

3. How does this melody move?

   a. upward ↗

   b. downward ↘

   c. repeats on the same pitch →

   d. upward then downward ↗↘

4. Which rhythm do you hear?

   a. 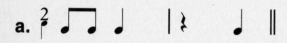   **c.**

   b.    **d.**

5. What pitches do you hear?

   a. 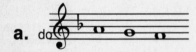   **c.**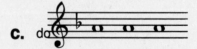

   b.    **d.**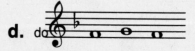

(See answers at the back of this book.)

Make Your Own Rhythm Pattern

- Put 2 eighth notes (♫) in 2 or 3 boxes below.

- Put a quarter note (♩) in 2 or 3 different boxes.

- Put a quarter rest (𝄽) in the other boxes.

Create a melody for your rhythm using the bells *do*
(F), *re* (G), and *mi* (A).

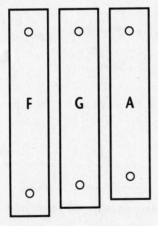

Write what you played on the staff.

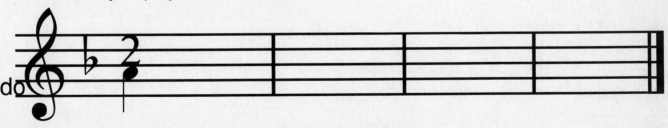

Add a surprise to your melody by playing a part
of it louder!

RESOURCE MASTER 2•1 Practice

Moving Rhythms

1. Cut out the pictures. Make a sidewalk by placing them in any order.

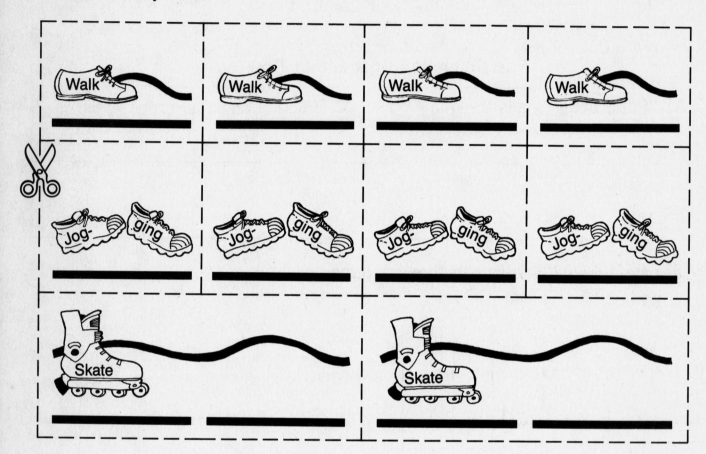

2. Now ask a friend to clap the steady beat. You say your sidewalk rhythm.

3. Clap the beat as a friend steps the rhythm.

walk	=	one step to the beat
jog-ging	=	two steps to the beat
skate	=	one step to two beats

Verses and Refrains

Listen to someone read this poem.

Look at the four sections. Write *verse* under each

verse. Write *refrain* under each refrain.

The Umbrella Brigade from *Tirra Lirra*

A. "Pitter patter!" falls the rain
On the school-room window-pane.
Such a splashing! such a dashing!
Will it e'er be dry again?
Down the gutter rolls a flood
And the crossing's deep in mud;
And the puddles! oh, the puddles
Are a sight to stir one's blood!

_____

B. But let it rain
Tree-toads and frogs,
Muskets and pitchforks,
Kittens and dogs!
Dash away! splash away!
Who is afraid?
Here we go,
The Umbrella Brigade!

_____

C. Pull the boots up to the knee!
Tie the hoods on merrily!
Such a hustling! such a jostling!
Out of breath with fun are we.
Clatter, clatter, down the street,
Greeting everyone we meet,
With our laughing and our chaffing
Which the laughing drops repeat.

_____

D. So let it rain
Tree-toads and frogs,
Muskets and pitchforks
Kittens and dogs!
Dash away! splash away!
Who is afraid?
Here we go,
The Umbrella Brigade!

_____

—*Laura E. Richards*

Macmillan/McGraw-Hill

(See answers at the back of this book.)

Name_____

"Foot" Puzzles

Trace these notes.

Walk   Jog- ging   Skate

Color in the noteheads for the walk and the jogging rhythm.

Write the notes for the rhythm next to each "foot" puzzle.

1.

Walk   Walk   Skate _____

2.

Jog-ging   Jog-ging   Walk   Walk _____

3.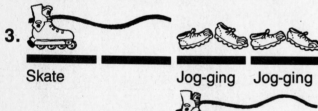

Skate   Jog-ging   Jog-ging _____

4.

Jog-ging   Jog-ging   Skate _____

A **tie** (⌣) between two quarter notes (♩ ⌣ ♩) tells you that the quarter notes sound for two beats, or a half note (♩). Write these patterns using half notes.

5. ♩ ♩ ♩ ♩ ♩ ♩   = _____

   Walk skate   walk skate

6. ♩ ♩ ♩ ♩ ♩ ♩   = _____

   Skate   skate   walk walk

(See answers at the back of this book.)

Deta, Deta

do re mi so la

Write the pitch syllable under each note.

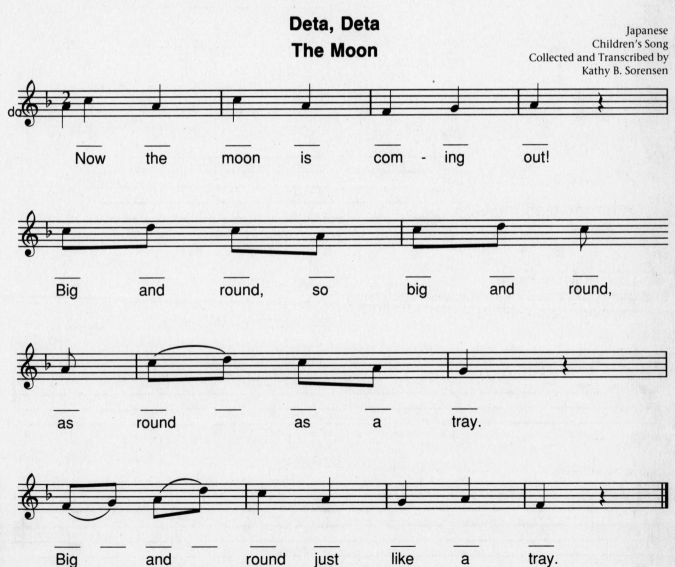

Deta, Deta
The Moon

Japanese
Children's Song
Collected and Transcribed by
Kathy B. Sorensen

Now the moon is com - ing out!

Big and round, so big and round,

as round as a tray.

Big and round just like a tray.

(See answers at the back of this book.)

Patterns in Melody

Write the correct pitch syllable. Then write whether
the note is **in a space** or **around a line**.

1.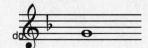

_____

2.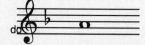

_____

3.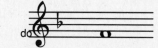

_____

4.

_____

5. Write the notes
do re mi so and
la on the staff.

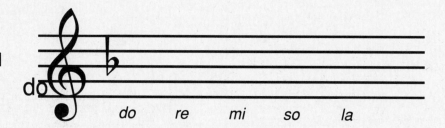

6. Use quarter notes (♩) and the pitches *do re mi
so* and *la* to write your own melody.

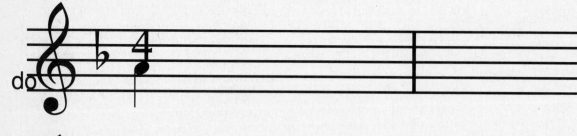

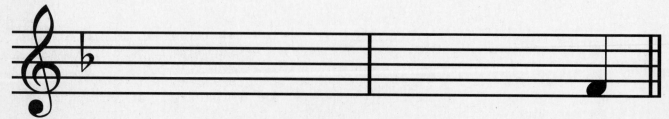

(See answers at the back of this book.)

Macmillan/McGraw-Hill

Night Watch
by Anthony Holborne

USING RESOURCE MASTER 2•6

DIRECTIONS:

Distribute a copy of the Resource Master to each child. Have children identify each brass instrument on the listening map. (two trumpets, French horn, trombone, and tuba) Point out the dynamic markings and have the children tell the meaning of each. Ask the children to name the lettered sections they see on the map. (two A sections, two B sections, and two C sections) Note the different carriages of each section and how they show the dynamic changes.

(The first A section carriage is larger than the second, because it is louder. The B section carriages start large and get smaller, because there is a decrescendo, and the C section carriages start small and get larger because there is a crescendo.) You may wish to have children color each A carriage one color, each B carriage another color, and each C carriage yet another color to highlight the form.

Check It Out

1. In which order do you hear the verse and refrain?

   a. refrain verse verse refrain   **c.** verse verse refrain refrain

   b. verse refrain verse refrain   **d.** refrain verse refrain verse

2. Which rhythm do you hear?

   a.

   b.   **c.**

            d.

3. What pitches do you hear?

   a.    **c.**

   b.   **d.**

4. Which melody do you hear?

   a. 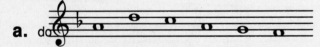   **c.**

   b. 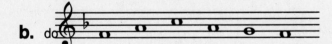   **d.**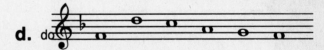

(See answers at the back of this book.)

RESOURCE MASTER 2•8 Assessment

Traveling Melody

Clap this rhythm. Say *walk* for ♩ , *jogging* for ♫ ,

and *skate* for ♩ ; say nothing on 𝄽

Create a melody for the rhythm using the pitches *do*
re mi so and *la*. Write the pitch syllables on the lines above.

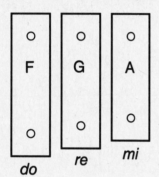

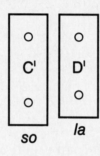

Now write your melody on the staff.

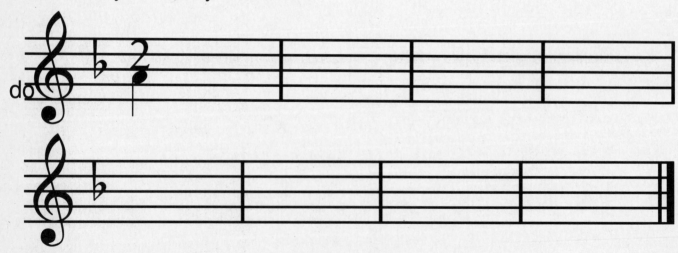

Choose a partner, and take turns playing each
other's melody.

Macmillan/McGraw-Hill

Name _____

Bate, bate

Clap the beat as you say the "Bate, bate" words.

| Ba | – | te, | ba | – | te, | | cho | – | co | – | la | – | te, |

| Con | | ar | – | roz | y | | con | | to | – | ma | – | te |

| U | – | no, | | dos, | | | tres, | | | CHO, |

| U | – | no, | | dos, | | | tres, | | | CO, |

| U | – | no, | | dos, | | | tres, | | | LA, |

| U | – | no, | | dos, | | | tres, | | | TE, |

| Cho | – | co | – | la | – | te, | | cho | – | co | – | la | – | te, |

| Cho | – | co | – | la | – | te, | | cho | – | co | – | la | – | te. |

RESOURCE MASTER 3•2 Practice

Conducting "Rattlesnake Skipping Song"

Draw arrows to show the downbeats (↓) and
upbeats (↑).

Listen to "Rattlesnake Skipping Song" as you
conduct the downbeats and upbeats.

Macmillan/McGraw-Hill

Name_____

Adding Bar Lines

1. Write the bar lines in this music in ⅞· meter.

a.

b.

c.

2. Write the bar lines in this music in ⅞ meter.

a.

b.

c.

(See answers at the back of this book.)

Row, Row, Row Your Boat

Circle the unequal rhythms in this song.

Row, Row, Row Your Boat

Traditional Round

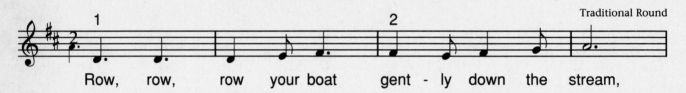

Row, row, row your boat gent - ly down the stream,

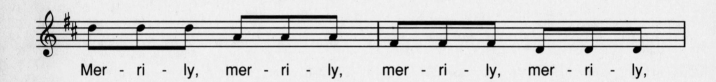

Mer - ri - ly, mer - ri - ly, mer - ri - ly, mer - ri - ly,

Life is but a dream.

(See answers at the back of this book.)

Name_____

"Bate, bate" in Equal Rhythm

Clap the beat as you say the "Bate, bate" words in an equal rhythm.

Macmillan/McGraw-Hill

"Bate, bate" in Unequal Rhythm

Clap the beat as you say the "Bate, bate" words in an unequal rhythm.

Name _____

Three Rides at the Park
by Linda Williams

USING RESOURCE MASTER 3·7

DIRECTIONS:

Distribute a copy of the Resource Master to each child. Have children find sections that are the same and sections that are different. (The three A sections, shown by the merry-go-round, are the same; the roller coaster B section and the Ferris wheel C section are different.) Have children name the form before listening. (A B A C A) Have them listen for the ostinato, or the repeating sounds, in each section. Explain that elements of all three sections are heard in the final section. You may wish to have children color all three A sections one color and each of the other sections contrasting colors to highlight this form.

Name _____

Pitch Practice

1. Match the pitch syllables to the staff notation.
Write the letters.

a. *do so mi re do* _____

b. *do la₁ so₁ la₁ do* _____

c. *do la so mi do* _____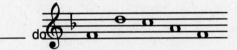

d. *mi do la₁ do mi* _____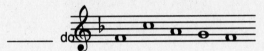

2. Write the notes to match the pitches below the staff.

a.

do   la,   so,   do

c.

mi   re   do   la,

b.

do   la   so   do

d.

do   re   mi   do

(See answers at the back of this book.)

Check It Out

1. Which of these has an equal rhythm?

    a.   **b.**   **c.**

2. Which of these has an unequal rhythm?

    a.   **b.**   **c.**

3. Which rhythm do you hear?

a.

b.

c.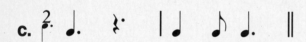

d.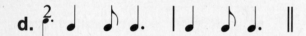

4. Choose the pitches you hear.

a. 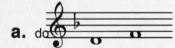   **c.**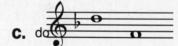

b.    **d.**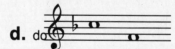

5. Which melody do you hear?

a.    **c.**

b. 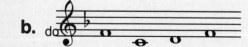   **d.**

(See answers at the back of this book.)

Macmillan/McGraw-Hill

Name _____

Everyday Music

Make your own eight-beat pattern. Write one of these rhythms on each line. Write the movement under it.

Rhythm:

♩.	♩ ♪	𝄽.
walk	skip - ping	rest

Movement:

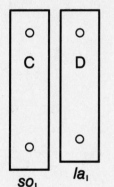

Use the bells *so₁ la₁ do re mi so la* to add a melody. Begin and end on *do* (F).

C	D		F	G	A	C'	D'
so₁	*la₁*		*do*	*re*	*mi*	*so*	*la*

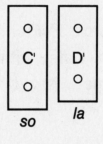

Write your melody on the staff.

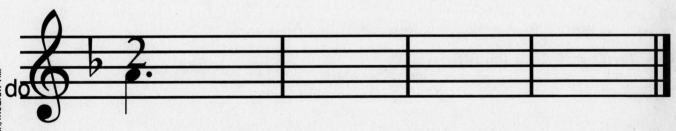

Play your melody while others perform your movement pattern.

Macmillan/McGraw-Hill

Four Syllables

1. Plan a trip from California to Florida.
   Stay overnight in some states with four-syllable
   names. Create a tongue twister by writing some
   four-syllable state names.

   _____   _____

   _____   _____

2. Write some of your favorite four-syllable words to
   create a rhythm pattern.

   _____   _____

   _____   _____

Macmillan/McGraw-Hill

Name _____

Stepping, Skipping, Repeating

A melody can:

- **Step** higher or lower to the next pitch.
- **Skip** higher or lower over one or more pitches.
- **Repeat** on the same pitch.

Circle the word that best describes how the melody moves.

1. stepping   skipping   repeating

2. stepping   skipping   repeating

3. stepping   skipping   repeating

4. stepping   skipping   repeating

5. stepping   skipping   repeating

(See answers at the back of this book.)

Macmillan/McGraw-Hill

RESOURCE MASTER 4•3 Practice

We're Off to See the Wizard

Draw phrase marks over the phrases you hear.

We're Off to See the Wizard

Words by E. Y. Harburg
Music by Harold Arlen

Follow the yellow brick road, Follow the yellow brick road,

Follow, follow, follow, follow, follow the yellow brick road.

Follow the rainbow over the stream,

Follow the fellow who follows a dream.

Follow, follow, follow, follow, follow the yellow brick road.

(See answers at the back of this book.)

Name _____

Overture to *The Marriage of Figaro*
by Wolfgang Amadeus Mozart

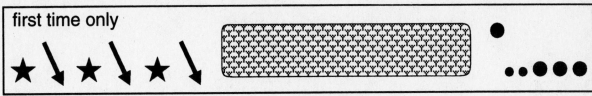

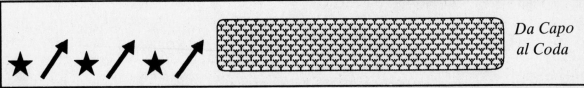

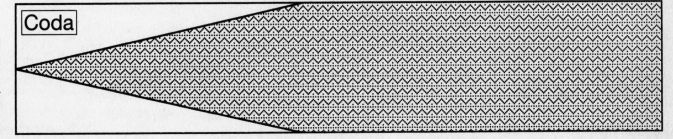

USING RESOURCE MASTER 4•4

DIRECTIONS:

Distribute a copy of the Resource Master to each child. Explain that the characters on this listening map are, in order of appearance: Figaro, a servant; Susanna, a maid to whom Figaro is engaged; Cherubino, a young man; and the Count. All appear in the story of Mozart's opera *The Marriage of Figaro*. The first box represents the fast note theme shown in the pupil book, and shows Figaro running. The second box shows Susanna with eyes closed for the quiet part of this theme, and with eyes wide open when the music gets suddenly loud. After these two themes are repeated, an interlude is heard, shown by the long shallow box. A picture of Cherubino hiding behind a chair follows.

This represents the suspenseful mood of the c section. Next, Cherubino clicks his heels, to represent the sudden *forte* notes in the d section. Box e shows the Count. He represents chromatic music. There is a repeated ascending pattern represented by the stairs. The peaceful mood of section f is shown by Figaro and Susanna together. Point out the *Da Capo al Coda* (go back to the beginning and follow to the coda) after the next interlude. Note: the last box of the first row and the interludes are heard only the first time; the last time box f is heard, it is followed by the coda. You may wish to have children color the map to show form.

Name_____

Presto Change-0

Are you a great magician?

Find out by changing one beat in line 1 from ♩ to  ♫ or from ♫ to ♬ . Write your answer on line 2. Continue to change one beat per line. If line 8 is  ♬ ♬ ♬ ♬ ,  then you are a great magician!

1. _____ _____ _____ _____

2. _____ _____ _____ _____

3. _____ _____ _____ _____

4. _____ _____ _____ _____

5. _____ _____ _____ _____

6. _____ _____ _____ _____

7. _____ _____ _____ _____

8. _____ _____ _____ _____

Choose a line to play as a rhythmic ostinato for "Salamanca Market."

RESOURCE MASTER 4•6 Practice

Reading Sixteenth Note Patterns

1. Cut out the patterns to make flashcards.

2. Work in pairs. Clap one pattern. Did your partner guess the pattern?

Name

Different *Dos*

Sometimes *do* is in a different place.

Do is on the second line.

do | do re mi so la

Do is on the first space.

do | do re mi so la

Do is on a ledger line.

do | do re mi so la

Write the missing pitch syllables in these examples.

1.

_____ _____ _____ _____ _____ _____ *do'*

2.

do

_____ _____ _____ _____ _____ _____ *do'*

3.

do

_____ _____ _____ _____ _____ *do'*

4.

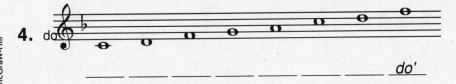

_____ _____ _____ _____ _____ _____ _____ *do'*

Macmillan/McGraw-Hill

(See answers at the back of this book.)

Pentatonic Cut-Up

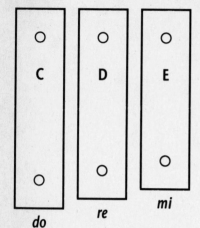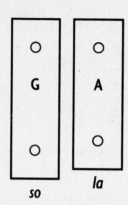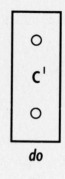

Form a group. Use these bells to play these melodies.

Listen to another group play their melody and guess the song title.

(See answers at the back of this book.)

Use with page 157. • Grade 3

Macmillan/McGraw-Hill

Name_____

What *Shall* We Do?

Create your own rhythmic answers to this question.

$\frac{4}{4}$ ♩ ♫ ♩ ♫ | ♩ ♩ ♩ ‖

What shall we do   with the   old sow's hide?

Write your answers in the spaces below.

  |

  |

  | ‖

Ask a friend to say your rhythms using these words.

♩ = hen   ♬ = cockadoodle   ♫ = rooster   ♩ = egg

A Musical Question to Answer

- Clap this rhythmic question.

- Create your own rhythmic answer by writing one of these rhythms in each of the boxes below.

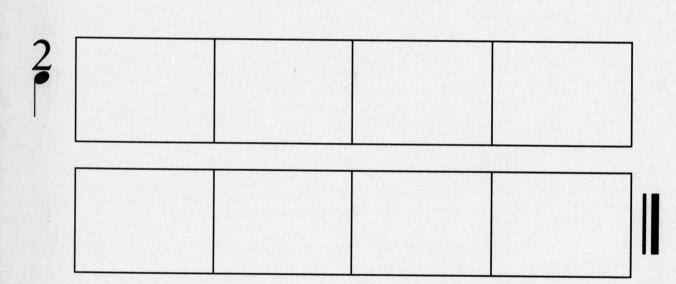

- Now clap the question.
- Have a friend clap your answer.

Name _____

Los mariachis
Mexican Folk Music

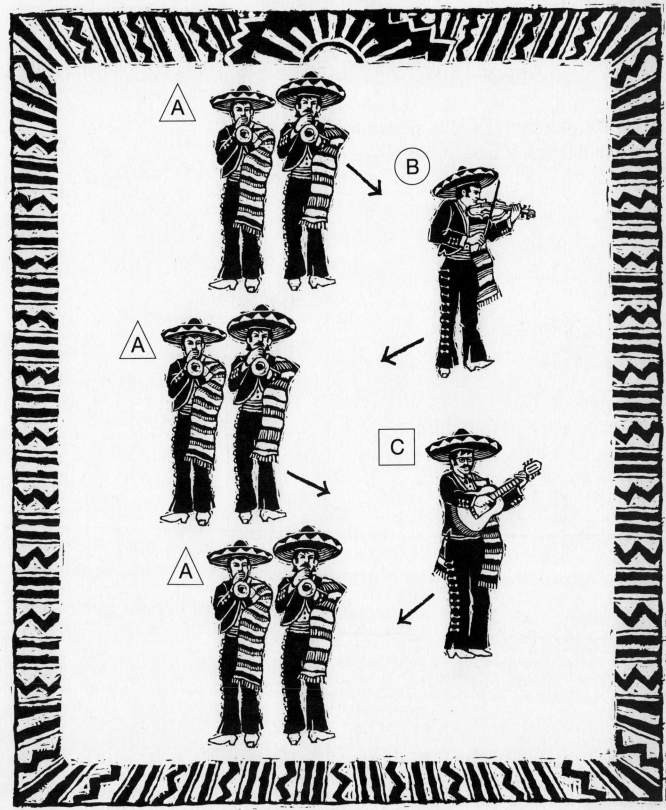

USING RESOURCE MASTER 4•11

DIRECTIONS:

Distribute a copy of the Resource Master to each child. Have children identify the rondo form by finding the number of A section pairs of trumpet players (three), and the contrasting sections (one B and one C section, shown by a violinist and a guitar player, respectively). You may wish to have children color the A sections one color and the other two sections contrasting colors to highlight the form.

Name _____

Rondo Round-Up

Help this rancher with his round-up.
Cut out and arrange his dog, cows,
and cowhand in rondo form.

(See answers at the back of this book.)

Check It Out

1. Circle the beat on which you hear four sixteenth notes.

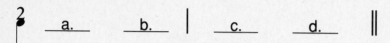

2. Choose the rhythm you hear.

a.

b.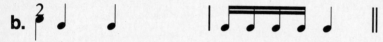

c.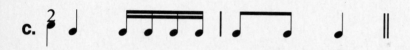

d.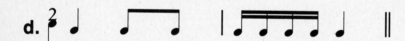

3. How many phrases do you hear?

   a. two   **b.** three   **c.** four   **d.** more than four

4. Which pitches do you hear?

a.    **c.**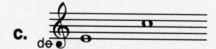

b.    **d.**

5. Choose the example you hear.

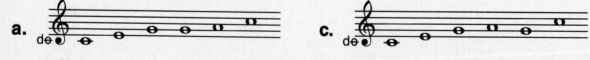

a.   **c.**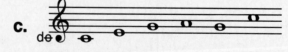

b. 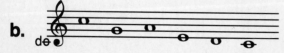   **d.**

(See answers at the back of this book.)

Use with page 168. • Grade 3

Name _____

Write a Musical Background

Write one of these rhythms on each line below.

With a partner, put your rhythms together to make a sixteen-beat rhythm pattern. Decide how to play your rhythm on the bells *do* (C) and *do*' (C'). Write your piece on the staff below.

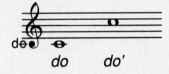

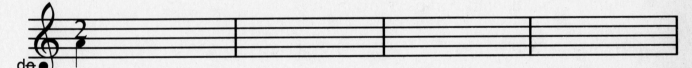

Play your piece while someone else sings one of these songs.

• "The Old Sow's Hide"

• "Salamanca Market"

• "I'll Rise When the Rooster Crows"

Four Beat Sweep

Sweep, Sweep Away
Creole Folk Song

Sweep, sweep, sweep a - way,

Sweep the road of dreams,

People say that, in the night,

The turtle will talk, it seems.

The turtle will talk, it seems.

- Listen to "Sweep, Sweep Away." Draw a
  bar line (|) at the beginning of each measure
  to divide the words into four-beat groupings.

- Draw phrase marks (⌒) over each phrase.

- Circle all of the words sung on a downbeat.

- Box all of the words sung on an upbeat.

- Which phrases start on weak beats or upbeats?

_____

_____

_____

Write an imaginary conversation two turtles
had on a warm summer night in Louisiana.

(See answers at the back of this book.)

Use with page 182. • Grade 3

Accompany Me to Sandy Land

Listen to "Sandy Land" and circle the words that are accompanied.

1. I make my living in the sandy land,
   I make my living in the sandy land,
   I make my living in the sandy land,
   Oh ladies, fare you well.

2. They raise big taters in the sandy land,
   They raise big taters in the sandy land,
   They raise big taters in the sandy land,
   Oh ladies, fare you well.

3. Sift the meal and save the bran,
   Sift the meal and save the bran,
   Sift the meal and save the bran,
   Oh ladies, fare you well.

4. One more river I'm bound to cross,
   One more river I'm bound to cross,
   One more river I'm bound to cross,
   Oh ladies, fare you well.

Color only the instruments which can play chords to accompany "Sandy Land."

(See answers at the back of this book.)

Name_____

RESOURCE MASTER 5•3 Practice

Eggbeaters

Each rhythm below is missing one or more notes.
Complete each one by drawing:

- a dotted half note (♩.) in the box when three
  beats are missing, or

- a whole note (○) when four beats are missing.

Hint! There are six dotted half notes and six whole notes missing.

1.

2.

3.

4.

5.

6.

Clap the completed rhythms.

Bonus: Which lines contain one dozen beats? _____ and _____.

(See answers at the back of this book.)

Macmillan/McGraw-Hill

Use with page 190. • Grade 3

Syllable Sweep

- Write in the pitch syllables for one of these phrases
  of "Sweep, Sweep Away."

- Sing the phrase with pitch syllables for some friends.

- They sing back your phrase with the correct words from the song.

Pentatonic

so, do re mi so la

Sweep, Sweep Away

Creole Folk Song

Sweep,   sweep,   sweep a - way,

Sweep   the   road   of   dreams,

Peo - ple   say   that,   in   the   night,

The   tur - tle will   talk,   it   seems.

The   tur - tle will   talk   it   seems.

(See answers at the back of this book.)

RESOURCE MASTER 5•5 Practice

Decisions

Calvin can't decide whether to write his rhythm in $\frac{3}{4}$ or $\frac{4}{4}$ meter. His music teacher said his rhythms work in $\frac{3}{4}$ **or** $\frac{4}{4}$ meter. But Calvin isn't quite convinced.

Is Calvin's teacher correct? Draw bar lines in the examples below to find out.

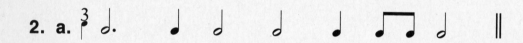

How would you perform these rhythms differently in $\frac{3}{4}$ or $\frac{4}{4}$?

_____

_____

(See answers at the back of this book.)

A Tale of Two Potato Farmers

Find out what happened to these two farmers by
writing either B, A, or G in the blanks.

B   A   G

Two pot__to farmers met on the road while he__ din__ to market.

E__ch pulled a l__r__e c__rt filled with their crop. They stopped to

__ __ __ __nd __r__ __ __bout who h__d the __i__ __est

pot__toes. "Why, my pot__toes __re the __ i __ __est," cried the first

farmer. "The s__nd w__s rich __nd the sun w__s __ri __ht. I can

make five __ __ __s of french fries with just one of my potatoes!"

"Just three of mine will fill __ ten pound __ __ __ ," said the second farmer.

(See answers at the back of this book.)

A Tale of Two Potato Farmers (page 2)

Just then, the sky turned d__rk and ___ torn__do touched the earth.

It picked up the two f__rmers and their crops and whirled them throu__h

the sky. When at l__st they were set ___ __ck on the ___round, they

couldn't ___elieve their eyes. Their potatoes had been sm__shed and

whirled into a creamy heap! "What will we do now?" cried the f__rmers.

They looked up to see the people from town come runnin__ down the

ro__d with forks, milk, and ___utter. What a fe__st they h__d!

M__shed potatoes! Enou__h to feed everyone in town!

(See answers at the back of this book.)

Macmillan/McGraw-Hill

A Recorder in the Sandy Land

- Finger B on the recorder with your left thumb and first finger.

- Put the mouthpiece between your lips and gently say *duh* as you blow. How long can you hold this pitch?

- Use your left hand second finger to cover the next hole and play A.

- Next, play G by covering the next hole with the left hand third finger.

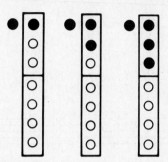

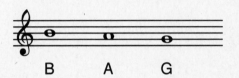

B   A   G

Now clap these rhythms.

Play each of these rhythms on the pitch B, then A, then G. Finally, play the tinted pitches on page 203 as your class sings "Sandy Land."

RESOURCE MASTER 5•8 Practice

A Recorder, a Bonefish, and a Bluebird

Work with two friends.

• Together, play the rhythm of the first three lines of this speech piece on the pitch B. Play the last line as written.

• Have each person in your group choose one of the first three lines. Try playing your line on just one pitch, or use all three!

B A G

• Write what you played. Perform your melodies for the class. Have everyone in class play line four.

Bonefish, Bluebird

Speech Piece by Ruth Hamm and
Isabel McNeill Carley
Words Adapted by MMH

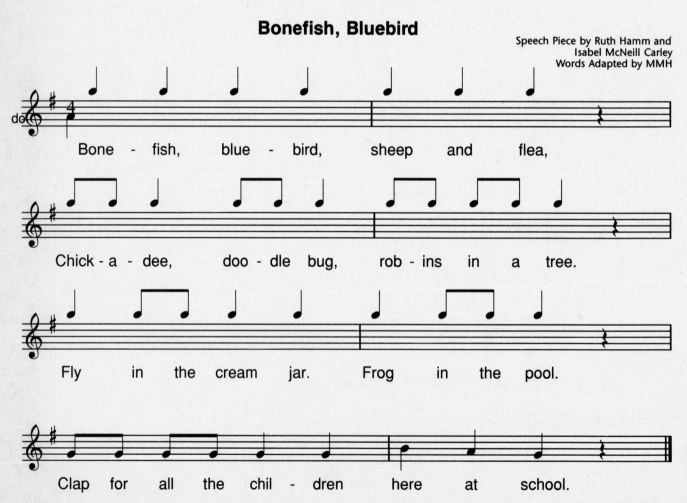

Bone - fish, blue - bird, sheep and flea,

Chick - a - dee, doo - dle bug, rob - ins in a tree.

Fly in the cream jar. Frog in the pool.

Clap for all the chil - dren here at school.

Melodic Ostinato for "Ton moulin"

Create your own ostinato for "Ton moulin."

- Choose from these rhythms:

  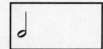

- Use your rhythm to write a melody. Choose
pitches from the G chord for measures 1, 2,
and 4. Choose pitches from the D chord
for measure 3.

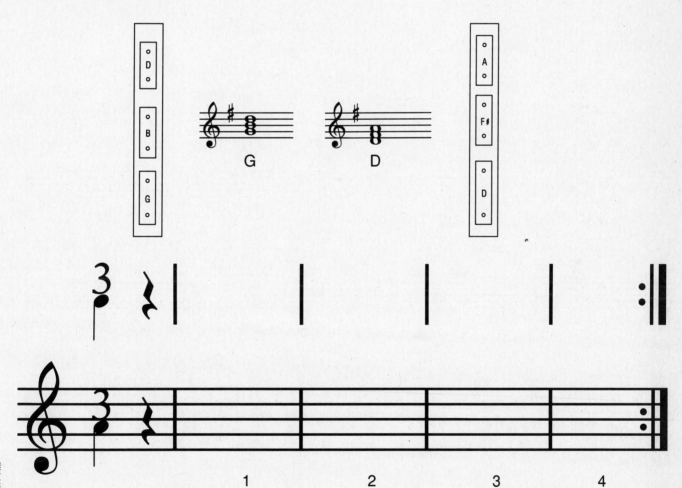

Perform your melodies as an ostinato
accompaniment for "Ton moulin."

Name _____

Check It Out

1. Which of these melodies has groups of three ($\frac{3}{4}$ meter)?

   a.   **b.**   **c.**

2. Which of these melodies has groups of four ($\frac{4}{4}$ meter)?

   a.   **b.**   **c.**

3. Which of these melodies starts on an upbeat?

   a.   **b.**   **c.**

4. Which of these melodies starts on a downbeat?

   a.   **b.**   **c.**

5. In which measure do you hear the dotted half note?

   a.   **b.**   **c.**   **d.**

6. In which measure do you hear the whole note?

   a.   **b.**   **c.**   **d.**

7. Which rhythm do you hear?

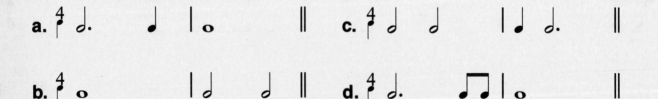

(See answers at the back of this book.)

Macmillan/McGraw-Hill

Name

Create Ostinato Accompaniments

Write one of these rhythms in each measure below.

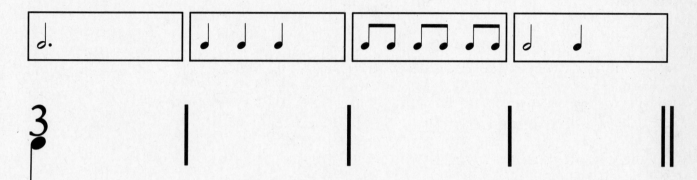

Choose an unpitched instrument, such as a drum.
Play your ostinato as an accompaniment to
"Cuequita de los coyas" or "Tititorea."

Now create an ostinato to accompany
"Sweep, Sweep Away." Choose from these rhythms
to fill in the measures below.

Name_____

Portfolio Option

Write the number 3 or 4 in the blank to match the
number of beats in these rhythms.

_____ 1.

_____ 2.

_____ 3.

_____ 4.

_____ 5.

_____ 6.

_____ 7.

_____ 8.

Create a four measure rhythm in either $\frac{4}{4}$ or $\frac{3}{4}$ meter
by choosing any of the above patterns, or write a
"Mabel, Mabel" rhythm from page 197.

Play your rhythm using the pitches B A and G on bells or recorder.
Write the meter and the melody you created on this staff.

(See answers at the back of this book.)

Name _____

I Got a Letter

Use this form to write a letter to a friend. Fold the
form into three parts and fill in the addresses on
the other side. Your letter might tell your friend of
some news that made you:

1. happy   **2.** sad   **3.** mad   **4.** excited

Fold---

Dear _____,

_____

_____

_____

_____

_____

_____

Fold---

_____

_____

_____

_____

_____

(Your name)

Fold---

Your address

_____

_____

_____

Friend's address

_____

_____

_____

Fold---

Singing with Feeling

Good News

Good news, chariot's comin'

Good news, chariot's comin'

Good news, chariot's comin'

And I don't want it to leave me behind.

- Read the words and describe the mood of the song.

- Choose words to sing staccato (·), legato (⌒), or marcato (>). Mark the words, then sing the song following your markings.

- Try singing the song fast, medium, or slow. Try starting slow and getting faster. Mark the words with a tempo you like.

- Mark the words with the dynamics of your choice. Try loud (f) or soft (p), or try singing with a crescendo (◁), or decrescendo (▷).

- Practice singing the song with all of the markings. Then perform your version for the class.

Macmillan/McGraw-Hill

Name_____

Four Faces of a Friend

Happy

Sad

Mad

Excited

Practice saying each of these sentences four different ways.

"I'm taking my little brother to the movies."

"My neighbor is moving away."

"Did you hear that noise?"

"Yesterday was my birthday."

Choose one of the sentences and say it for a partner.

Can your partner guess which expression you used?

Did you use a loud or soft voice?

_____

Did you say the words fast or slow?

_____

Did you say the words smoothly (legato), short and lightly (staccato), or with

extra force (marcato)? _____

Use with page 220. • Grade 3

March of the Wooden Soldiers from *Album for the Young*

by Piotr Ilyich Tchaikovsky (arr. Dubinsky)

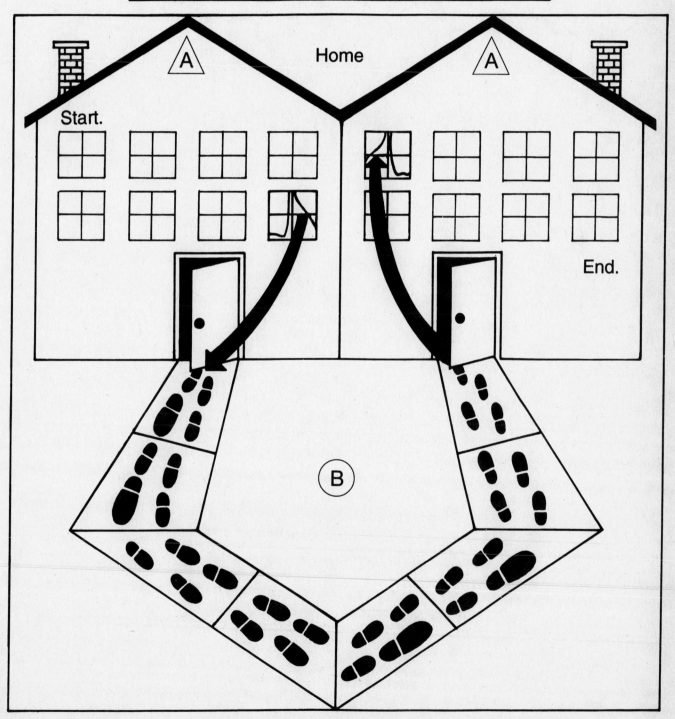

USING RESOURCE MASTER 6•4

DIRECTIONS:

Distribute a copy of the Resource Master to each child. Explain that the beats in this music are grouped in sets of four. Each window represents one measure, each pane representing one beat. Each sidewalk section represents one measure, and each footprint on the sidewalk represents one beat. Point out that some footprints are larger (louder) than others. To follow the map (moving away from and back to the home tone) proceed from the left house, reading left to right, to the sidewalk, and to the upper left corner of the house on the right, reading left to right, ending with the lower right window pane. You may wish to have children color the houses (A sections) one color, and the sidewalk (B section) a contrasting color.

Name _____

Changes in Style

19th-Century Chair

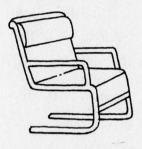

20th-Century Chair

Styles change over time. These pictures show how
some things might have looked 100 years ago. Draw how each looks today.

How might your favorite cartoon character have
looked 100 years ago? Draw a picture on the back of this paper.

RESOURCE MASTER 6•6 Practice

Pitch Stairs

Find *do* in "Killy Kranky" (page 232), then find *do*
in "Zudio" (page 235). Circle *do* on the pitch stairs
and on the staff.

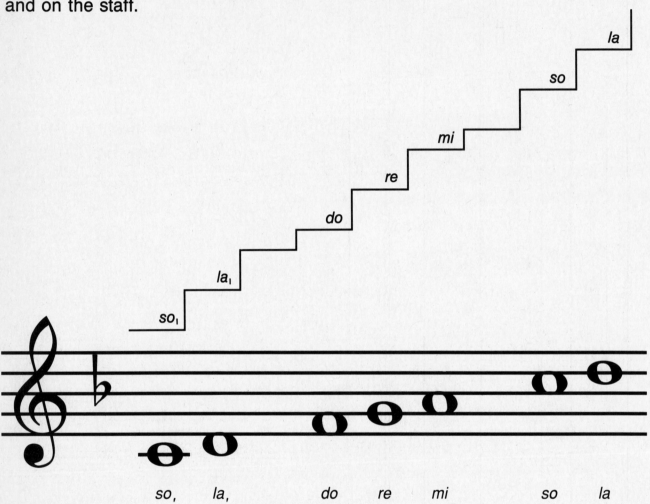

Draw an arrow pointing to the tonal centers of
"Killy Kranky" and "Zudio." Are they in the same
place? Most pentatonic songs end on the tonal center.

(See answers at the back of this book.)

Name _____

Using First and Second Endings

Create a version of "Old Man Moses" using first and second endings.

1. Write a "1" just before the first line of lyrics and a "2" just below the "1."

2. Copy the third line of lyrics right after the "2."

3. Draw a bracket (⌐————⌐) over the entire second staff with a "1." inside the left corner.

4. Draw a repeat sign (:‖) at the end of the second staff.

5. Draw a bracket (⌐————⌐) over the last staff with a "2." inside the left corner.

6. Cut out the first, second, and last lines of music and lyrics and paste them on a separate sheet of paper.

Sing the song following your new music.
Does it still sound the same?

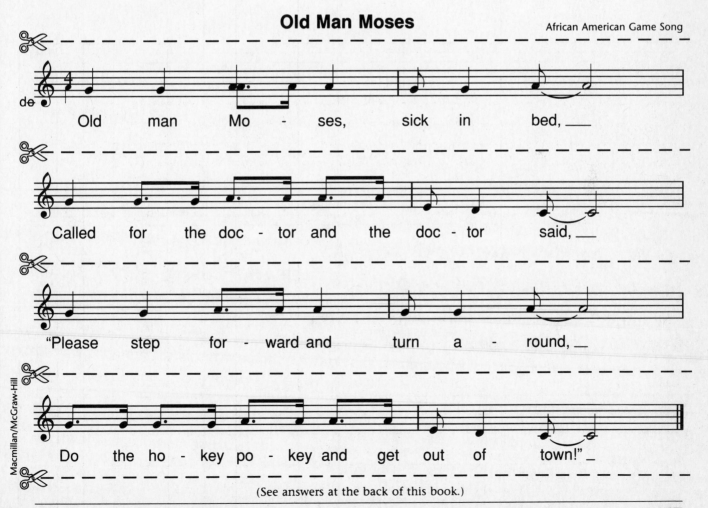

Old Man Moses

African American Game Song

Old man Mo - ses, sick in bed, ___

Called for the doc - tor and the doc - tor said, ___

"Please step for - ward and turn a - round, __

Do the ho - key po - key and get out of town!" _

(See answers at the back of this book.)

Macmillan/McGraw-Hill

Good News from a FAX!

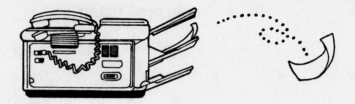

A FAX transmission can announce good news from a
person far away. Fill in each blank with B A G or F to
find the good news in each one of these FAX's.

I ___ound your pet.   I'll ___ rin___   her ___ ___ck   tod___y.

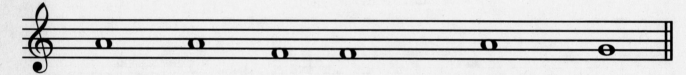

My p___rents s___y   it's ___ine ___or   you to st___y   the   ni___ht.

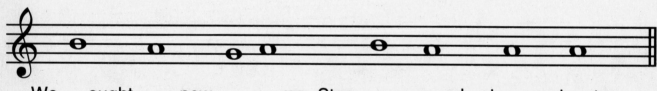

We ___ought ___ new ___ ___me. Stop ___y ___nd pl___y I ___ter.

Work in a group to create your own coded good news
FAX. Then give it to another group to decode.

(See answers at the back of this book.)

Name _____

Finding F G A on the Keyboard

✂ -

You can find the notes F G and A
on the staff and on the keyboard.

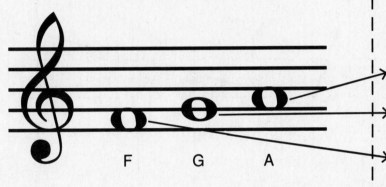

F   G   A

F is always to the left of the group of
three black keys. G and A are always just
to the right of F. Lay this cutout near the
keyboard to find as many groups of F G
and A keys as possible.

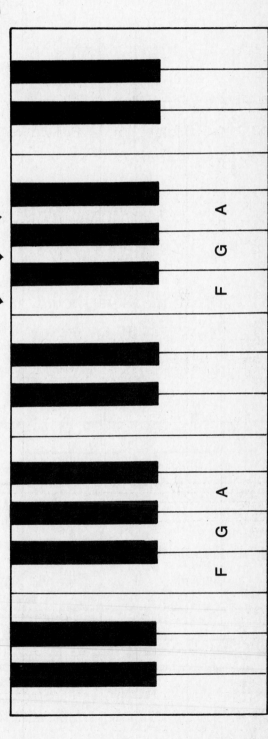

Write a Musical Letter

Use these four bells to create a new melody for
"I Got a Letter."

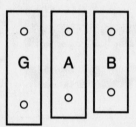

The second measure should end on *do re* or *mi.*
The sixth measure ends on low *la.* Draw in the note
heads for your melody on the staff below.

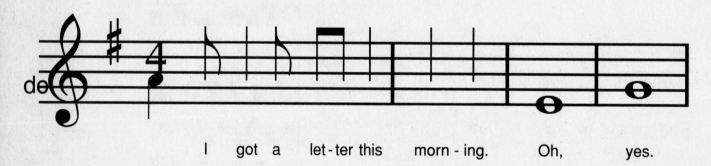

I got a let-ter this morn-ing. Oh, yes.

I got a let-ter this morn-ing. Oh, yes.

Now play your melody for a friend.

Macmillan/McGraw-Hill

Check It Out

1. How is this music sung?

   a. staccato   **b.** legato   **c.** marcato

2. How is this music sung?

   a. staccato   **b.** legato   **c.** marcato

3. How does this music end?

   a. on the tonal center   **b.** away from the tonal center

4. How does this music end?

   a. on the tonal center   **b.** away from the tonal center

5. Which melody do you hear?
   Is the tonal center of that melody *do* or *la₁*? Circle *do* or *la₁*.

a.

b.

c.

d.

(See answers at the back of this book.)

Express Yourself

Create a piece of music with first and second endings.

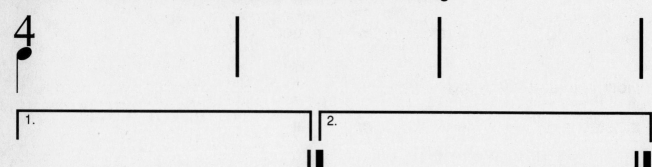

Choose some of these rhythms to write in the measures above.

Play your piece on instruments. Mark your piece with some of these expressive words.

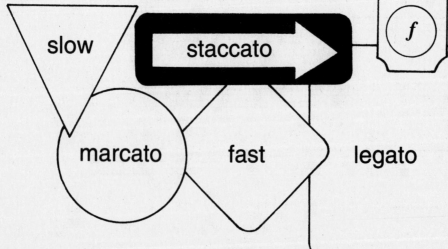

Perform your piece following your expressive markings.

Name _____

Melody Madness

Sing or play each of these patterns. Label the ones
that end on the tonal center with an "O." Label the ones
that end away from the tonal center with an "A."

1. ___    3. ___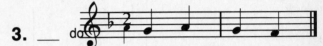

2. ___ 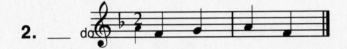   4. ___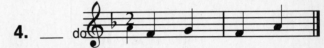

Play two of the patterns, one after the other.

Work in a group. Write some of the patterns in the
measures below, or write in your own patterns. Try
adding a repeat, or a first and second ending. Will
your piece end on or away from the tonal center?

Write in how you would like to play your piece: legato,
staccato, or marcato; forte or piano; fast or slow.
Play your piece then give it to another group to perform.

(See answers at the back of this book.)

Macmillan/McGraw-Hill

America, the Beautiful

Cut out these lines from "America, the Beautiful."
Arrange the lines in any order.
Try singing the song in this new order.
Which way do you like better? Why?

Write your own patriotic text for the melody of
"America, the Beautiful."

America, the Beautiful

Words by Katharine Lee Bates

O beautiful for spacious skies, For amber waves of grain.

For purple mountain majesties, Above the fruited plain.

America! America! God shed His grace on thee,

And crown thy good with brotherhood, From sea to
shining sea.

Patriotic Holiday Speech Piece

- Work in groups of three. Have each person choose one of the parts below.

- Practice saying the words and performing the body-percussion.

- Perform the three parts together. Listen for the changing body-percussion tone colors.

Part 1

La - bor Day, Co - lum - bus Day, *clap, clap, clap, clap.*

Part 2

Mar - tin Luth - er King, *stamp, stamp.* Lin-coln and Wash-ing - ton, *stamp, stamp.*

Part 3

Flag Day, *snap, snap, snap, snap.* Fourth of Ju - ly.

RESOURCE MASTER C•3 Patterns

Making Flags

Color this flag and cut it out.

Create your own flag design with your favorite shapes.
Cut it out.

Paste your flags to a straw or wooden stick.

Macmillan/McGraw-Hill

Name _____

Popcorn Party Pleasers

Use these seasonings from around the world to flavor
your popcorn.

Tex-Mex

1/3 cup olive oil or butter

1 tablespoon dry taco seasoning

2 tablespoons dried chives

15 cups popped popcorn

Warm the olive oil in a small saucepan. Add the
taco seasoning and dry chives and mix thoroughly.
Pour over popcorn and toss.

Asian

3 ounces chow mein noodles

3 tablespoons sesame seeds

1 tablespoon dried chives

1 tablespoon garlic powder

1/2 teaspoon ginger

8 cups popped popcorn

Combine all of the ingredients, then mix with popcorn.

Italian

1/3 cup olive oil or butter

2 teaspoons Italian seasoning

3/4 teaspoon garlic powder

1/4 cup grated Parmesan cheese

15 cups popcorn

Warm the olive oil in a small saucepan. Add the
Italian seasoning, garlic, and Parmesan cheese and
mix thoroughly. Pour over popcorn and toss.

Harvesting

Until the 1830s, grains such as wheat were harvested by hand. The wheat kernels were then separated from the stalks, a job requiring several steps. This whole process took many days. Today, large machines called combines can harvest wheat in just a few hours, combining all of the steps. In the United States, wheat harvest begins in June in the south and moves north during the summer months.

Most fruits, and many vegetables are still harvested by hand. Unlike grains, fruits and vegetables are sorted and packed for shipping. Those being sold as fresh produce must be handled carefully. In warm climates, fruits and vegetables can be harvested all year long. Modern methods of refrigeration and transportation provide these fresh foods for people all over the United States.

Choose one fruit, vegetable, or grain. Use your library to find out how that produce would be harvested. List the steps on the back of this page.

Macmillan/McGraw-Hill

St. Patrick's Day
Irish Folk Music

Introduction

a

4 times

a

a

b

a

b

a

USING RESOURCE MASTER C·6

DIRECTIONS:

Distribute a copy of the Resource Master to each child. Help children to identify the instruments on the listening map. (introduction: uillian pipes; then drum and violin) Explain that each symbol, a shamrock or a Tam o'Shanter, represents one beat, and that the beats are grouped in sets of four. Point out the repeat signs, and tell children that the music within them is heard four times. You may wish to have children color all shamrocks green, showing the a sections, and all Tam o' Shanters red, showing the b sections, to highlight the form.

Accompaniment Parts for "Treasure Chests"

Play one of these parts as your class sings "Treasure Chests."

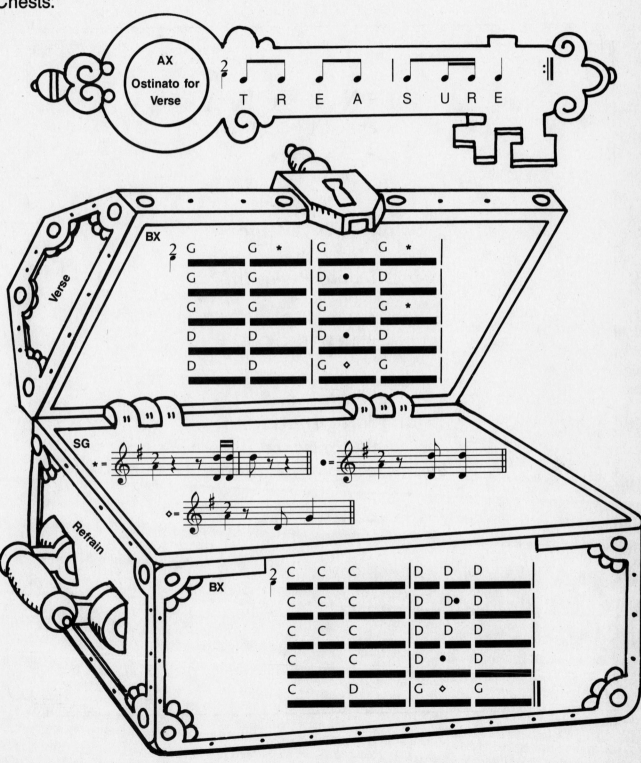

Violin Recital

Follow the program as you listen to the violin recital.

VIOLIN RECITAL
Presented by Midori

Caprice in A Minor
(excerpts)
by Niccolò Paganini

INTERMISSION

Sonata No. 8
for Violin and Piano
Allegro vivace
by Ludwig van Beethoven

Name _____

Putting on a Recital

Work with a group of friends to put on a recital.
Sign up for the jobs below.

Performer _____

Program Designer _____

Advertiser _____

Stage Manager _____

Ticket Taker _____

Usher _____

Intermission Planner _____

Fill in the blanks on these tickets. Then cut them out
and give them to your friends or parents.

Ticket	**Ticket**	**Ticket**
Date: _____	Date: _____	Date: _____
Time: _____	Time: _____	Time: _____
Place: _____	Place: _____	Place: _____
Event: _____	Event: _____	Event: _____
Ticket	**Ticket**	**Ticket**
Date: _____	Date: _____	Date: _____
Time: _____	Time: _____	Time: _____
Place: _____	Place: _____	Place: _____
Event: _____	Event: _____	Event: _____

Macmillan/McGraw-Hill

El grillo
by Josquin des Prez

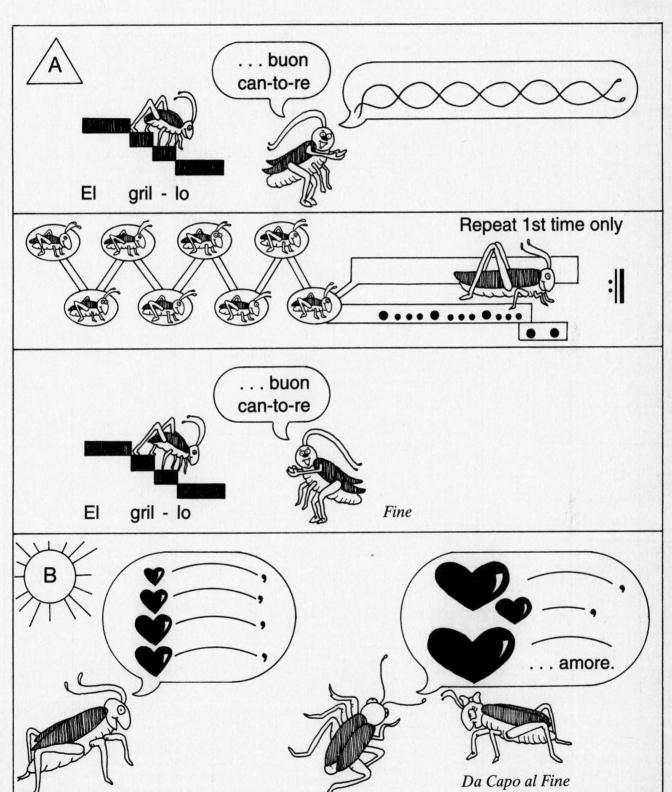

USING RESOURCE MASTER LA•3

DIRECTIONS:

Distribute a copy of the Resource Master to each child. Help children find how the cricket on the map shows the shape of the melody (descending notes in the beginning and third row, weaving up and down at the end of the first row, high-low changes in the second row). Have children find the A and B sections, the repeat signs, and the note to repeat the A section the first time only, as well as the *Da Capo al Fine* and *Fine* markings. Explain their meanings.

Explain that each curved line in the B section indicates one sung phrase, with a breath mark after it to show a slight break. The word "amore," or *love*, signals the end of the B section. Help children find the meaning of the B section (the cricket sings in the hot sun only for his sweetheart). You may wish to have children color the A section triangle one color, and the B section circle another color, to highlight the form.

Name _____

Minuet in G from *Notebook for Anna Magdalena Bach*, attr. to Johann Sebastian Bach

by Christian Petzold

KEY	one dot = downbeat in $\frac{3}{4}$

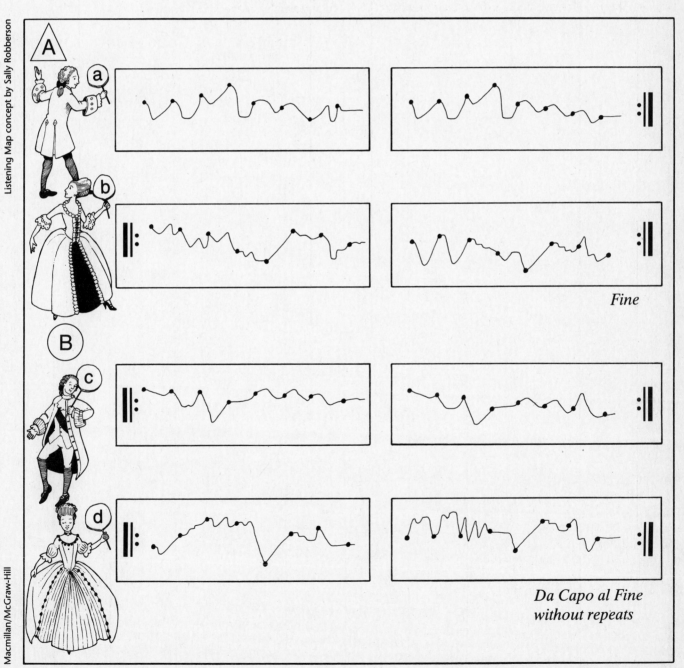

Fine

Da Capo al Fine
without repeats

USING RESOURCE MASTER LA·4

DIRECTIONS:

Distribute a copy of the Resource Master to each child. Have children find the A and B sections and the a, b, c, and d sections on the map. Tell children that each dot represents the first beat, or downbeat, of each measure, and that the shape of the melody is shown by the connecting lines. Point out the repeat signs, the *Da Capo al Fine without repeats* marking, and the *Fine* marking, and explain their meanings. (After the A and B sections are heard with all the repeats, the map continues with the A section without repeats and ends at the *Fine* mark.) You may wish to have children color the four sections of the listening map to highlight the form, making the a and b sections warm colors, and the c and d sections cool colors.

Name _____

Eine Kleine Nachtmusik, First Movement
by Wolfgang Amadeus Mozart

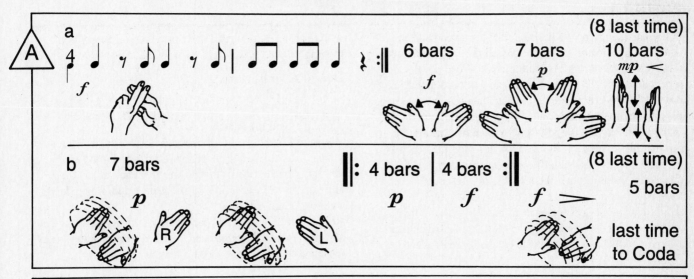

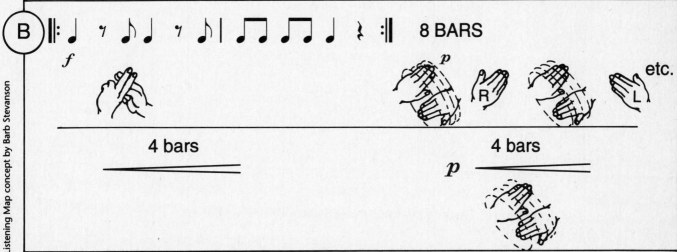

USING RESOURCE MASTER LA·5

DIRECTIONS:

Distribute a copy of the Resource Master to each child. Have children locate all A sections on the map (there are three), then the B section and the coda. Point out all repeat signs. Tell children that all parts without notation last the number of measures indicated above the movement pictures and/or dynamic indications. Have children locate all dynamic markings and tell what each one means. Point out that the last part of the first row lasts ten measures in all cases but the last time through, when it lasts for eight measures. Point out that the last part of the second row lasts five measures in all cases except the last time through, when it lasts for eight measures. Tell children to make their movements large for loud parts and small for quiet parts. You may wish to have children color the A sections one color, and the B section and the coda contrasting colors, to highlight the form.

Directions for hand movements:
Crossover: Hold hands with palms facing outward at eye level on beats 1 and 3, then move hands to make an X shape on beats 2 and 4.
Waves: Move hands (with palms facing outward) from side to side, beats 1 and 2 to left and beats 3 and 4 to right.
Chops: Place hands so that palms face each other, then alternate moving left hand up on beats 1 and 3, and down on beats 2 and 4.
Rolls: Roll hands around each other on beats 1 and 2, then alternate extending right hand to side on beats 3 and 4 and left hand to the side on beats 3 and 4.

Name _____

Clair de lune from *Suite bergamasque*
by Claude Debussy

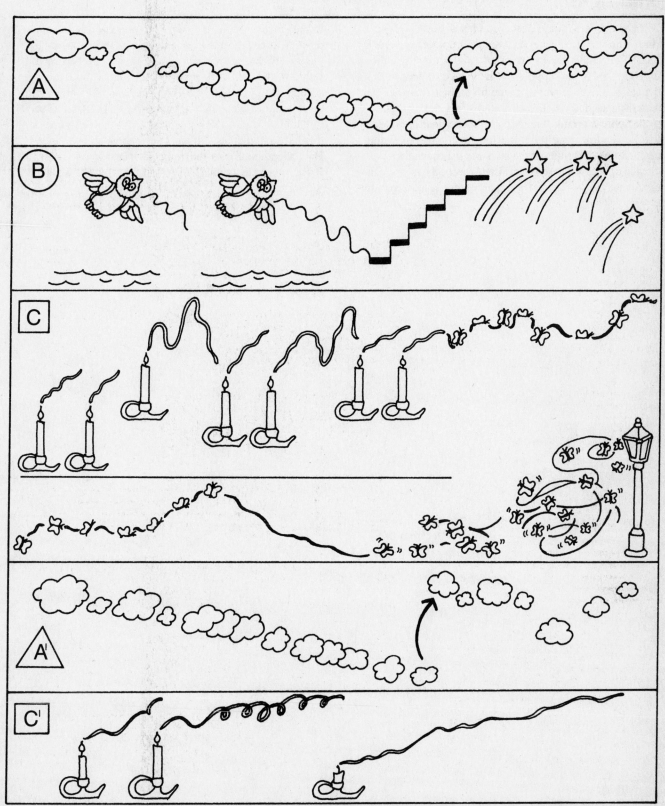

DIRECTIONS:

Distribute a copy of the Resource Master to each child. Have children find the lettered sections on the map. (A B C A' C') Explain that the different sizes of clouds in the A section show the shape of the melody, duration, and dynamics. Each cloud is a group of notes, rather than one note. The second row contains an owl for each initial higher phrase chord, with melodic shape lines after each one. Each step in the stairs is a low note in the ascending musical line. The tails of the stars are the ascending pitches up to each high pitch. The C section has one candle for the beginning of each small phrase. The smoke follows the shape of the melody. After seven of these candle phrases, the night moths take over, ending in a flurry by the streetlight for an extended period of time. Next is the return of the melody from the A section, without the second row of owls, and so on. The final row contains just three candles, the smoke showing the shape of the C section melody again. You may wish to have children color this listening map as if it were set against a night sky. Have them color both the A and A' triangles one color, the B section circle another color, and the C and C' squares yet another color.

Name _____

Cortège
by Lili Boulanger

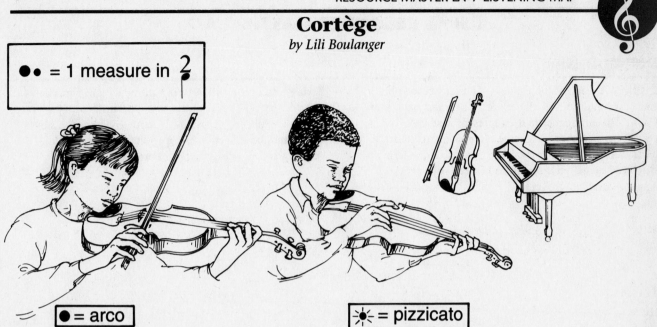

●● = 1 measure in ²⁄₄

● = arco   ☀ = pizzicato

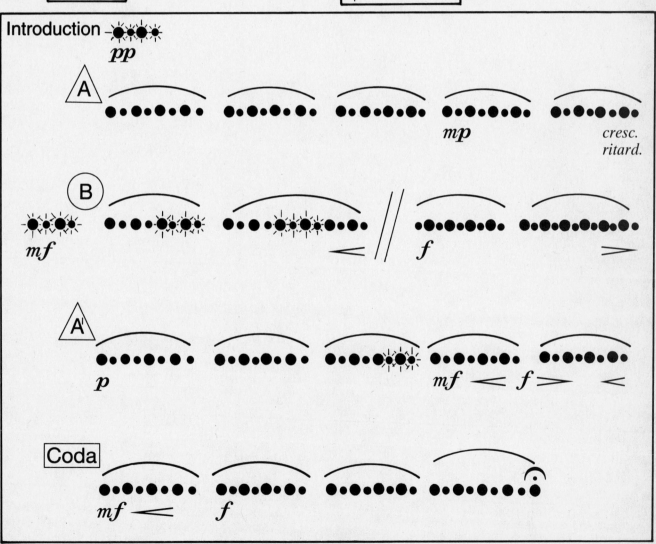

USING RESOURCE MASTER LA•7

DIRECTIONS:

Distribute a copy of the Resource Master to each child. Have the children find all the sections on the map (A B A' Coda). Explain that each dot represents one beat and each curved line represents a phrase of music. A plain dot represents *arco* playing (with the bow on the string), and sparkles around a dot represent *pizzicato* playing (plucked string). Have the children find all the dynamic markings on the map and tell the meaning of each. You may wish to have the children color the A section triangles the same color and the B section circle and coda rectangle contrasting colors to highlight the form.

Name _____

"Classical" Symphony, Third Movement
by Sergei Prokofiev

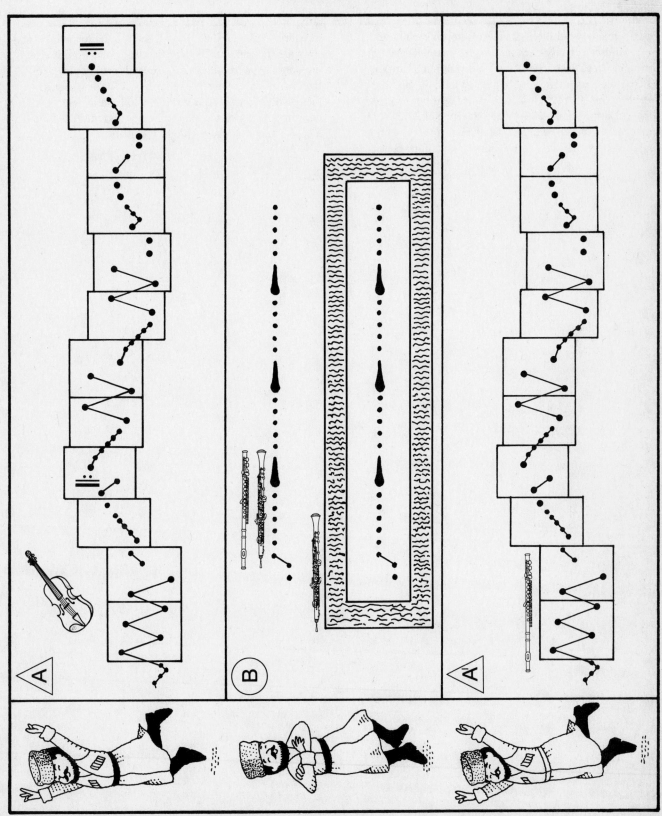

USING RESOURCE MASTER LA·8

DIRECTIONS:

Distribute a copy of the Resource Master to each child. Help children identify each instrument pictured. (violin, flute and oboe, oboe, flute) Have the children locate the lettered sections on the map. (A B A') Explain that the dancer to the left of each section is to illustrate the mood; it is not part of the listening map. Have the children find the section with repeat signs. (latter part of the A section) Explain that each tinted square contains one four-beat measure. Point out that in the B section the top and bottom rows are the same, except for the decorative border around the bottom row representing a second melody played by the oboes. This map shows the shape of the melodies of the entire selection. You may wish to have the children color the A and A' sections one color and the B section a contrasting color to highlight the form.

The Electric Cat

A musical about finding friends
Words and Music by Linda Worsley

CAST

Kurt, the narrator

A family who has just
moved to town:
Shawn
Shawn's Mother
Shawn's Father

Hairy, the cat

Teacher

Sandy, a friend of Shawn's
Friends 1, 2, and 3
The Chorus

(The curtain goes up on a scene with children "frozen" in various poses of play.)

Kurt *(to audience):* Let me tell you about Shawn and her electric cat. Shawn wasn't always my friend, and the cat wasn't always electric. Here's how it happened.

(Children unfreeze and sing)—

SONG *(Kurt and Chorus):* "After School"

(The rumble of thunder. A flash of lightning. The children look up, hold out their hands to feel the rain, and shout, "It's raining!" They run offstage.)

(We see Shawn, sitting on the porch, looking forlorn.)

Father *(from inside the house):* Come on in, it's raining!

Shawn *(calling to him):* It's dry here on the porch.

Mother *(from inside the house):* Shawn, you haven't seemed to feel well since we moved here. You need some vitamins.

Shawn *(over her shoulder):* Really . . . I'm fine. Just watching the rain.

Father: How was your day?

Shawn: It was OK. I got a B plus on my math test. And I stayed in at P.E. and helped the Teacher. I didn't feel like playing.

Father (*sighs, shakes his head*): I'm happy about your math grade, but I do wish you would try to get out and play with some of the kids. Exercise is what you need.

Shawn (*to herself and the audience*): Kids! Math! I hate school. School is so lonesome! Not like my school in Springville. I had *friends* in Springville.

Teacher (*to self and the audience*): I've never taught a child like Shawn before. So lonely and sad all the time! She needs confidence. I wish she'd make friends.

SONG (*Shawn, Mother, Father, Teacher*):
"All I Need Is a Friend"

(*As the song ends, Shawn "sees" Hairy the cat come out of the house and mimes picking the animal up.*)

Shawn: Hey, Hairy! Here, kitty, kitty. . . (*strokes the cat*) Good old Hairy. You're my only friend. You don't seem to miss Springville at all.

(*Loud thunder. Another flash of lightning. The cat "jumps" out of Shawn's arms, across the yard, and up a tree. All of this is accomplished in mime by Shawn, who jumps, opens her arms, and follows the cat with her hands and eyes.*)

Shawn: Hairy! Don't go up that tree ... (*Looking up, getting wet, and going back to the porch*) Hairy, you dumb cat! That's the tallest tree in town! (*Goes inside*) Mom! Dad! Hairy's up a tree and won't come down!

Kurt: Shawn's mom and dad didn't know what to do. They all came out in the rain and called and called, but the cat wouldn't come down. By nightfall, the rain had stopped, but the cat still hadn't come down.

(*Shawn and Mother and Father have come back out and mimed calling the cat down from the tree. Finally, Shawn is alone under the tree. Sandy comes up to her.*)

Sandy: Hi.

Shawn *(still looking up at the cat):* Hi.

Sandy *(shyly):* Um . . . *(looking up)* Looking for something?

SONG *(Shawn):* "My Cat's Gone Up in a Tree" (Verse 1)

Sandy: That *is* a problem. We had a kitty go up a tree once, and my grandma said, "Don't worry . . . I've never seen any kitty bones up in trees. She'll come down!" And sure enough she did! It was just a little tree, though. *(looking up)* This tree must be a hundred feet tall!

Shawn: Yeah. Thanks. *(freezes)*

Kurt: Well, the cat didn't come down. In fact, next morning, Hairy had climbed even higher. After school the cat was still up there. That's how I got in on it. I was having a bad day myself . . . even without a cat in a tree. I ran into my friend Sandy . . .

(Kurt starts to walk across stage and is joined by Sandy. Shawn is in the background, still looking up at the tree.)

Sandy *(to Kurt):* Do you want to come over to my house and . . .

Kurt: Nah . . .

Sandy: Want to go biking? . . . It's sunny . . . we could . . .

Kurt: Biking is no good . . .

Sandy: Boy, are you crabby! . . . What's the matter?

Kurt *(crossly):* This is my third bad day in a row. I'm crabby for a reason.

SONG *(Kurt, Sandy, Chorus):* "Crabby"

Kurt *(noticing Shawn looking up in the tree):* Isn't that the new kid in our class?

Macmillan/McGraw-Hill

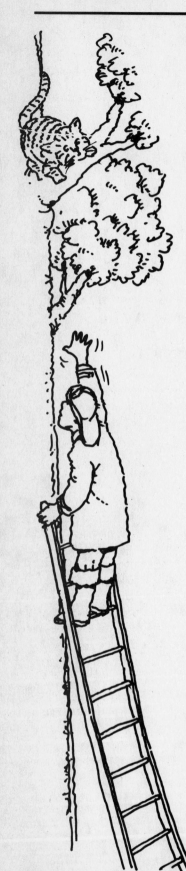

Sandy: Yes . . . and her cat still hasn't come down . . . *(walking over to Shawn, looking up in the tree)* Still up there?

Shawn: I'm afraid so . . .

SONG *(Shawn, Sandy):*
"My Cat's Gone Up in a Tree" (Verse 2)

Kurt: Wow, that would make me *really* crabby!

Sandy: Grandma says that cats love fish. Let's put some fish under the tree and see if the cat comes down to eat it.

Shawn: Good idea! Let's see if my mom has some tuna . . . My name's Shawn . . . what's yours? *(They walk into the house "talking" in mime.)*

Kurt *(to the audience):* So we tried tuna fish. The cat didn't budge. By now he was up so high in the tree, he probably couldn't even smell it!

(Shawn and Sandy mime as much of this as there is time for. Then they freeze.)

Then we called the fire department, but their ladder wasn't tall enough. The next day, we were all pretty discouraged. It was Saturday, so I went to see how the cat was doing . . .

(Kurt joins Shawn and Sandy under the tree.)

Kurt: Still no luck? *(all shake their heads)*

(Two other children join them.)

All: Hi! What's going on?

Kurt: Well, we have this little problem . . .

SONG *(Shawn, Sandy, Kurt):*
"My Cat's Gone Up in a Tree" (Verse 3)

Friend 1: My dog ran away once, but we got him back. He doesn't know how to climb trees.

Friend 2: I'm glad I have a goldfish. He never runs away.

(Another child joins them.)

Friend 3: Hi, What's going on?

Kurt: This is Shawn ... you know, her family just moved here. But she has this problem ...

SONG *(Shawn, Sandy, Kurt, and the two friends):* "My Cat's Gone Up in a Tree" (Verse 4)

Friend 1: There must be some way to get him down? We ought to be able to think of something!

Sandy: Well, there's a whole bunch of us now ... and you know what my grandmother always says ...

Kurt: No, but I'll bet you're going to tell us ...

SONG *(Sandy, Others, Chorus):* "Two Heads Are Better Than One"

Kurt: This is no help! I think that cat has decided to stay in the tree!

Sandy: We'll think of something ... My grandma always says ...

Kurt: Look, Sandy. Bring your grandma here in a few weeks, and we'll show her some kitty bones up in the tree.

Friends 2 and 3: Well, we have to go. Shawn, do you want to come over and help us fix our bikes?

(Loud clap of thunder! Flashes of lightning! The cat runs down the tree and lands in Shawn's arms ... all mimed by the children.)

All Children: Look, here comes the cat.

(Mother comes to the door and sees what is happening.)

Shawn (cradling the cat): Hey, Hairy! You decided to come down.... about time!

Kurt *(to Sandy):* What would your grandmother say about that?

Sandy: She'd probably say Hairy is an *electric* cat! You have to turn him on!!

Mother *(coming over and taking the cat):* I think this electric cat is going to be an indoor cat from now on. No more trees, Hairy! Shawn, would you like to have your friends over for a treat? We've made pizza.

Friend 1: I'm your friend, Shawn!

Friend 2: I'm her friend, too!

Friends 1 and 3: Hey, wait a minute, we're all her friends. *(Shawn's friends all talk at the same time, then everyone freezes)*

Kurt *(to audience):* And that's the story of how Shawn's electric cat helped her make friends in a new place.

Kurt: Anyway, since I am Shawn's *best* friend...

Sandy: But I was her friend *first!*

Shawn *(To Sandy):* Well, I know what your *grandmother* would say ...

SONG *(Shawn, Entire Cast):*
"Two Friends Are Better Than One"

(The curtain falls. "After School" is played as the cast takes its bows.)

Macmillan/McGraw-Hill

Name _____

The Goat Who Couldn't Sneeze

Adapted by James Abar from a Mexican Folk Tale
Music by Juan Orrego-Salas
Words by Mary Goetze

CAST

Ramón, the goat who couldn't sneeze
Four other Goats
Chorus, a herd of goats
Policía 1 and 2
Bear
Wildcat
Deer

Flower Seller
Miller
Teacher
Doctor
Chorus, villagers
Six Bees

SCENE I

(High in the Sierra Madre Mountains)

Ramón: Señores y Señoras, as leader of our herd, I announce the final event of our fiesta—the great sneeze-off.

SONG *(Chorus):* "Ah-choo"

Goats 1 and 2: Ramón, aren't you going to join the great sneeze-off?

Ramón: Not right now.

Goats 3 and 4: You're our leader. You should join us.

Goats 1 and 2: You didn't join us last year in the sneeze-off. Or the year before.

Ramón: Well, to be honest, I have a problem.

SONG *(Ramón):* "Song of the Goat"

Goats 1 and 2: But everyone can sneeze!

Ramón: Except me!

Goats 3 and 4: But you're our leader. What'll the other animals think of us if they find out our leader can't even sneeze?

Goat 4: I can sneeze. AHHH-CHOOOOO!

All: Oooooo! That was a great sneeze.

Goat 1: You're the winner of the sneeze-off!

Goat 2: Maybe you should be our leader.

Goat 4: Maybe I should. Everyone follow me.

Ramón: Wait, I can sneeze. Listen: Ah-ah-ah-ah-ah, nuts!

Bear *(enters yawning):* Did someone say nuts? Where are they? Walnuts are my favorite.

Ramón: Oh, Buenos días, Señor Bear. Sorry to wake you up. I was just trying to sneeze.

Bear: I'm not quite awake. I didn't hear you right.

Ramón: I can't sneeze.

Bear: But everyone can sneeze, you just do this. *(loudly)* AH-CHOOOO!

Deer *(very nervous):* Wh-wh-what's that noise?

Wildcat: Who's that *(like a cat)* YEEOOWLING?

Ramón: Bear was showing me how to sneeze, Señorita Deer.

Deer: Well, when I want to sneeze, I look at a bright light and then ah-choo!

Wildcat: Purrrfect! Everyone can sneeze. Even kittens can sneeze.

Ramón: Let me try that. *(looking at a light)* Ah-ah-ah— no good!

Goats 3 and 4: You're just not paying attention. Now listen.

SONG *(All):* "The Bear and the Wildcat" (Verses 1 and 2)

Ramón: I think, ah-ah, maybe ah-ah, this is it ah-ah-ah-ah.

Wildcat: Purretty strange not be able to sneeze. I have to go home and look after the kittens. Adiós, Ramón. *(exits)*

Bear: I'm off to find something to eat. Adíos.

All: Adíos.

Goat 4: I don't think Ramón should be our leader. I won the sneeze-off. Everyone, follow me.

All: Adíos, Ramón. *(exit)*

Deer: This is terrible. Try a little pepper under your nose.

Ramón: Do you have any pepper?

Deer: No, I'm sorry.

Ramón: Maybe if I left the mountain and went into town, I could find someone to teach me how to sneeze.

Deer: You mean, leave the mountain? All by yourself?

Ramón: Would you go with me?

Deer: OOOH, I'd be too afraid. You have to cross the bridge to get into town.

Ramón: That's right. So?

Deer: Aw, haven't you heard of the troll and the three billy goats Gruff?

Ramón: I really think that was just made up. Don't you?

Deer: I-I-I don't know. W-w-w-hat if there is a troll?

Ramón: There are no such things as trolls.

Deer: Well, I don't want to find out if there are or aren't!

Ramón: Gracias, thank you for helping. Adíos amiga.

Deer: Adíos. Good luck, amigo.

Ramón: I'm off to town to learn to sneeze. *(Ramón walks a few steps.)* Oh, here's something to graze on. I think I'll graze for a while. *(Every time Ramón steps, the Bees buzz offstage. They stop buzzing when he stops walking.)* Over there's the bridge to town. There are no such things as trolls.

Bees *(offstage, softly):* Buzzzzz.

Ramón: Who's under the bridge? There are no such things as trolls.

Bees *(offstage, a bit louder):* Buzzz.

Ramón: Hello? Is there a troll under there? There are no such things as trolls.

Bees *(offstage, very loudly):* BUZZZ.

Ramón: Troll or no troll, I feel a sneeze coming on. Ah-ah-ah-ah mi! What's going on in town? It's a fiesta!

SCENE II

(A small Mexican village. Villagers enter singing, with colored streamers and banners. They are playing maracas, tambourines, and güiros.)

SONG (Villagers): "Welcome Song"

Ramón: Buenos días! Could someone teach me to sneeze?

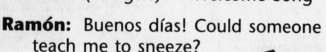

Flower Seller: I'm a flower seller. I can teach you how to grow things. Maybe you should ask the miller. He is very smart.

Ramón: Buenos días, Señor Miller. Could you teach me to sneeze?

Miller: I could teach you how to grind masa for tortillas, but not how to sneeze. Maybe you should ask the policía. They always help people.

Ramón: Officers, could you help me?

Policía 1: What's the trouble? Have you been robbed?

Ramón: No.

Policía 2: What is it? Don't be shy. We're here to help.

Ramón: Could you teach me to sneeze?

Policía 1: No, but if there are any people in town who could help you, they are the teacher and the doctor.

Ramón: Let's go find them.

Policía 1 and 2: Here they come right now.
(The teacher and the doctor enter.)

SONG *(All):* "Teacher, Doctor"
("The Bear and the Wildcat," verses 3 and 4)

Teacher: Adíos amigos.

Doctor: Adíos amigos.

(The teacher and the doctor exit.)

Ramón: Well, no one here can teach me to sneeze, so I'll just go home. Gracias, everybody. Adíos.

All: Adíos. *(exit)*

Miller: It's a long journey back to the mountains. Here are some tortillas with a little honey on them for you to eat on the way.

Flower Seller: Don't feel bad. Here are some flowers to cheer you up.

Ramón: Adíos. *(exit)*

**Miller and
Flower Seller:** Adíos. *(exit)*

SCENE III

Ramón: *(He stops to graze for a minute, thinking to himself.)* I give up. I can't go back home. All the goats will laugh at me. *(Every time Ramón steps, the Bees buzz offstage. They stop buzzing when he stops walking.)*

Bees *(offstage, softly):* Buzzzz.

Ramón: What's that buzzing sound? That's the same sound I heard coming from under the bridge. It keeps following me. *(taking a step)*

Bees *(offstage, more loudly):* Buzzzz.

Ramón: Who's there? There are no such things as trolls.

Bees *(enter, loudly):* BUZZZZZ.

Ramón: Bees!

Bees 1 and 2: B-b-buenos días. We followed you from town. We live under the bridge.

Ramón: I thought you were trolls.

Bees 3 and 4: There are no such things as trolls. We've been looking everywhere for you.

Ramón: How did you find me?

Bees 5 and 6: We followed the smell of the honey on the tortillas. And the smell of the flowers.

Ramón: What do you want?

Bees 1 and 2: We heard you can't sneeze. We can teach you. Do you have anything to pay for a lesson?

Ramón: No.

Bees 5 and 6: Sure you do. The honey. And the flowers.

Ramón: Here, take them. Now, please teach me.

SONG *(Bees):* "Song of the Bees"

Ramón: Ah-ah-ah-ah-chooooo!

SONG *(Everyone back home):* "What Was that Deafening Roar?"

Ramón: Ah-chooooo! Ah-ah-chooo!

SONG *(Ramón):* "I Made That Deafening Roar"

Ramón: I sneezed. Uh, oh, here comes another one. Ah-ah-ah-choooo.

SONG: "Song of the Goat" *(Reprise)*

GOAT 4: So you finally learned to sneeze. Big deal, I'm still the winner of the great sneeze-off. And I'm the new leader of the herd.

Ramón: Stand back, everyone. Ah-ah-ah-ah, chooooo!

Goat 3: That's the biggest and best sneeze we've ever heard. Ramón is the winner of the great sneeze-off!

SONG *(All):* "You Sneezed"

Ramón: Ah-ah-ah—

Goats 1, 2, 3: Look out everyone!

Ramón: AH-AH-AH-AH-AH—

All: Whew!

Ramón: CHOOOOOOOOOOO!

(The entire cast enters and bows to the audience.)

Student _____ Date _____

Portfolio Evaluation Form

Directions: For each student, review the contents of the portfolio and assign a score of 1–4 for each criterion listed below. Determine a summary score for the entire portfolio, based on Criteria 1–12 (or more).

CONTENTS	Needs to Improve	Fair	Good	Excellent
1. **Completeness.** Meets all requirements.	1	2	3	4
2. **Variety.** Includes a variety of pieces.	1	2	3	4
3. **Organization.** Shows clear organizational plan.	1	2	3	4
4. **Volume.** Includes sufficient amount of work.	1	2	3	4
5. **Focus/Purpose.** Meets intended purposes.	1	2	3	4

ATTRIBUTES				
6. **Effort.** Demonstrates concerted effort.	1	2	3	4
7. **Quality.** Illustrates appropriate level of quality.	1	2	3	4
8. **Creativity.** Shows imagination and creative ideas.	1	2	3	4
9. **Risk-Taking.** Takes risks in creating/choosing works that go beyond minimum expectations.	1	2	3	4
10. **Growth.** Shows improvement.	1	2	3	4
11. **Reflection.** Shows signs of personal reflection.	1	2	3	4
12. **Self-Evaluation.** Shows awareness of strengths and weaknesses.	1	2	3	4

THINGS YOU'D LIKE TO ADD				
13. _____	1	2	3	4
14. _____	1	2	3	4
15. _____	1	2	3	4

SUMMARY SCORE

	Needs to Improve	Fair	Good	Excellent
Meets the requirements of program goals.	1	2	3	4

COMMENTS

Name _____

Student Assessment Cards

Directions: Have students complete one or more of these cards as an attachment for each item chosen for their portfolios.

Name of piece _____ Date _____

My description of this piece

Name of piece _____ Date _____

Why I like this piece

How I might change this piece

Name of piece _____ Date _____

What I learned from doing this

Name _____ Date _____

Interest Inventory

Put a check beside as many answers as you like.

1. I like to. . .

_____ listen to music   _____ move to music

_____ play music   _____ compose music

_____ sing songs   _____ perform for others

2. Types of music I like are. . .

_____

_____

_____

3. I'd like to know more about. . .

4. Here's an idea I'd like to try in music. . .

Name_____ Date_____

Self-Assessment Form

What I can do well	What I would like to do better
in listening	
in playing music	
in singing	
in moving to music	
in composing music	
in performing for others	

I'd like you to know. . .

Name _____ Grade _____

Music Log

Date	Title	What I Thought About It

Resource Master 1•2, Page 2

1. a. **2.** b. **3.** c.

4.

Rock - y moun-tain, Rock - y moun-tain,

Rock - y moun-tain high.

Resource Master 1•3, Page 3

2. a. rock rock rock mountain

b. rock *rest* mountain mountain

c. mountain mountain rock rock

d. rock *rest* rock *rest*

Resource Master 1•4, Page 4

1. a. 2   **c.** 5
b. 3   **d.** 1

2. a.   **c.**

b.   **d.**

3. *re do mi do*

Resource Master 1•5, Page 5

1. *mi re do*

2. *mi mi mi re re do*

3. c.   **5.** b.   **7.** e.

4. d.   **6.** a.

Resource Master 1•8, Page 8

Test A

1. b.   **2.** a.   **3.** a.   **4.** d.   **5.** b.

Test B

1. a.   **2.** b.   **3.** b.   **4.** c.   **5.** d.

Resource Master 2•2, Page 11

A. Verse   C. Verse
B. Refrain   D. Refrain

Resource Master 2•3, Page 12

1.

2.

3.

4.

5.

6.

Resource Master 2•4, Page 13

Line 1: *so mi so mi do re mi*
Line 2: *so la so mi so la so*
Line 3: *mi so la so mi re*
Line 4: *do re mi la so mi re mi do*

Resource Master 2•5, Page 14

1. *re*; around a line   **3.** *do*; in a space

2. *mi*; in a space   **4.** *la*; around a line

5.

do   re   mi   so   la

Answer Key

Resource Master 2•7, Page 17

Test A

1. b. **2.** a. **3.** d. **4.** c.

Test B

1. a. **2.** d. **3.** a. **4.** b.

Resource Master 3•2, Page 20

↓	↑	↓	↑
↓	↑	↓	↑
↓	↑	↓	↑
↓	↑	↓	↑

Resource Master 3•3, Page 21

1. a.

b.

c.

2. a.

b.

c.

Resource Master 3•4, Page 22

The unequal rhythms occur in measures 2 (first beat), 3, and 7.

Resource Master 3•8, Page 27

1. b.   d.   c.   a.

2. a.

do   la,   so,   do

b.

do   la   so   do

c.

mi   re   do   la,

d.

do   re   mi   do

Resource Master 3•9, Page 28

Test A

1. b.   **2.** b.   **3.** a.   **4.** b.   **5.** c.

Test B

1. c.   **2.** b.   **3.** d.   **4.** a.   **5.** d.

Resource Master 4•2, Page 31

1. stepping   **3.** skipping   **5.** stepping

2. repeating   **4.** skipping

Macmillan/McGraw-Hill

Resource Master 4•3, Page 32

Follow the yellow brick road, Follow the yellow brick road,

Follow, follow, follow, follow, follow the yellow brick road.

Follow the rainbow over the stream, Follow the fellow who follows a dream.

Follow, follow, follow, follow, follow the yellow brick road.

Resource Master 4•7, Page 37

1. *do re mi so la do'*   3. *do re mi so la do'*
2. *do re mi so la do'*   4. *so, la, do re mi so la do'*

Resource Master 4•8, Page 38

"Goin' to Ride Up in the Chariot"
"I'll Rise When the Rooster Crows"
"Wang Ü Ger"
"Salamanca Market"

Resource Master 4•12, Page 43

A B A C A

Resource Master 4•13, Page 44

Test A

1. a.   2. b.   3. b.   4. b.   5. d.

Test B

1. b.   2. c.   3. a.   4. d.   5. c.

Resource Master 5•1, Page 46

Sweep, sweep, sweep a way
Sweep the road of dreams,
People say that, in the night,
The turtle will talk, it seems,
The turtle will talk, it seems.

- The following phrases start on upbeats:
  People say that, in the night,
  The turtle will talk, it seems.
  The turtle will talk, it seems.

Answer Key

Resource Master 5•2, Page 47

1. I make my living in the sandy land,
   I make my living in the sandy land,

   (I make my living in the sandy land,
   Oh ladies, fare you well.)

2. They raise big taters in the sandy land,
   (They raise big taters in the sandy land,)
   They raise big taters in the sandy land,
   (Oh ladies, fare you well.)

3. Sift the meal and save the bran,
   Sift the meal and save the bran,
   (Sift the meal and save the bran,)
   Oh ladies, fare you well.

4. One more river I'm (bound to cross,)
   One more river I'm (bound to cross,)
   One more river I'm (bound to cross,)
   Oh ladies, (fare you well.)

Piano, *banjo*, and *guitar* can play chords to accompany "Sandy Land."

Resource Master 5•3, Page 48

Bonus: Lines 1 and 2

Resource Master 5•4, Page 49

Line 1: *do mi re do re*
Line 2: *mi mi mi re do*
Line 3: *do mi so la so mi do*
Line 4: *do mi mi so, so, so, do*
Line 5: *do mi mi so, so, so, do*

Resource Master 5•5, Page 50

The strong beat is always the first beat of each measure. In 3 meter, the beats are grouped in sets of 3. In 4 meter, the beats are grouped in sets of 4.

Resource Master 5•6, Pages 51 and 52

A Tale of Two Potato Farmers

Two potato farmers met on the road while heading to market. Each pulled a large cart filled with their crop. They stopped to gab and brag about who had the biggest potatoes. "Why, my potatoes are the biggest," cried the first farmer. "The sand was rich and the sun was bright. I can make five bags of french fries with just one of my potatoes!" "Just three of mine will fill a ten pound bag," said the second farmer. Just then, the sky turned dark and a tornado touched the earth. It picked up the two farmers and their crops and whirled them through the sky. When at last they were set back on the ground, they couldn't believe their eyes. Their potatoes had been smashed and whirled into a creamy heap! "What will we do now?" cried the farmers. They looked up to see the people from the town come running down the road with forks, milk, and butter. What a feast they had! Mashed potatoes! Enough to feed everyone in town!

Resource Master 5•10, Page 56

Test A

1. b.	**3.** a.	**5.** d.	**7.** a.
2. c.	**4.** c.	**6.** b.	

Test B

1. b.	**3.** b.	**5.** b.	**7.** c.
2. a.	**4.** a.	**6.** c.	

Resource Master 5•12, Page 58

1. 3	**3.** 3	**5.** 4	**7.** 4
2. 4	**4.** 4	**6.** 3	**8.** 3

Resource Master 6•6, Page 66

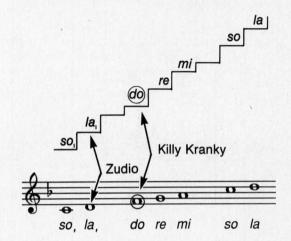

Answer Key

Resource Master 6•7, Page 67

African American Game Song

1. Old man Mo - ses, sick in bed, _
2. "Please step for - ward and turn a - round,

Called for the doc - tor and the doc - tor said, _

Do the ho - key po - key and get out of town!" _

Resource Master 6•8, Page 68

I found your pet. I'll bring her back today.

My parents say it's fine for you to stay the night.

We bought a new game. Stop by and play later.

Resource Master 6•11, Page 71

Test A

1. b.   **2.** a.   **3.** b.   **4.** a.   **5.** c. *do*

Test B

1. c.   **2.** b.   **3.** a.   **4.** b.   **5.** b. *la*

Resource Master 6•13, Page 73

1. O   **3.** O

2. O   **4.** A

Grade 3

Macmillan/McGraw-Hill